Small Prairie '4575 Class' 2-6-2T No 5542 is one of 11 examples of that class which escaped the cutting torch. 5542 is pictured at the Gloucester & Warwickshire Railway. *Pete Sherwood.*

Hard at work. The steam footplate crew aboard Stanier 'Princess Royal' 4-6-2 No 6201 Princess Elizabeth (LMS number) as 'she' climbs Shap (northbound).

During the same period passenger numbers dropped considerably as bus services in rural areas replaced trains and family car ownership became the norm. Commuter travel was perhaps the one area of rail travel which remained buoyant but electric traction, and the introduction of DMUs, rapidly led to a replacement of steam on even those services. There was of course a last week, and indeed a last day for steam, but it is fair to draw the conclusion that the end of steam effectively started with the inception of BR on 1 January 1948.

The progressive withdrawal of steam locos became the catalyst for new undertakings. The preservation movement was born! At first driven by a love of steam, and later by all things 'railway', it has grown steadily from that day to the present time. Encouraged by the sterling efforts of thousands of volunteers a phoenix has risen from the cold ashes that was BR steam. That high flying bird is Railway Preservation. Supporting that

BRITISH STEAM
PRESERVED

CAMBRIAN
COAST
EXPRESS
7812

89
A

ISHED IN GREAT BRITAIN   £7.99

BN 978-1-906167-11-0

781906 167110

KEITH LANGSTON

ILLUSTRATED COMPREHENSIVE LISTING OF EX BRITISH RAILWAYS STEAM LOCOMOTIVES

FOREWORD

On the evening of 11 August 1968 the last standard gauge steam locomotive running on British Railways dropped its fire. A significant act? Yes. It was the end of an era for machines that had supported the industrial revolution and played a part in building the British Empire.

Those who loved steam crossed the country to see these magnificent machines working out their last days. Not only were steam locomotives being dispatched to the scrapyards, the whole ambience of the railway was being changed in the name of progress. Old Victorian stations, engine sheds, signalboxes, crossing keepers' houses were demolished one by one. For many enthusiasts it was 'their' hobby which they saw rapidly disappearing.

It was the 1960s. Flower power, pop music, student unrest and civil rights were the issues with which the young became associated. People of the time had the confidence to make changes, this filtered through to the railway enthusiasts of Great Britain.

For some it was also time for action. Aware that no one else would help them keep their hobby alive, many rolled up their sleeves in the struggle to raise the money needed to drag the abandoned hulks out of the scrapyards. Dying skills were revived in order to restore rescued engines to their former glory. Some of the locos were once the pride of the nation, others simply the backbone of our rail transport system.

Britain now has a railway heritage collection like no other country in the World, thanks to the vast army of dedicated volunteers. Their unselfish dedication ensures that not only the hardware of the railways has been kept alive since 1968, a unique way of life has also been preserved.

Why do they continue to do it? Could it be the love of the railway, the passion of their particular interest, or camaraderie among the staff? A question not easily answered.

Dewi Jones
Traffic Manager
Severn Valley Railway

Cover image: Ex Great Western Railway 'Hall Class' 4-6-0 No 7812 Erlestoke Manor seen approaching Hampton Loade Station during the SVR September 2008 Gala Weekend.

CONTENTS
INCLUDE...

A Perceptive Images © 2008 Publication for Mortons Media Group.

Written compiled and edited by:
Keith Langston
Editorial assistant: David Anderson

Special thanks to guest photographers David Anderson, John Bowers, Barry Dewdney, David Gibson, Fred Kerr, Sue Langston, Paul Pettitt, Brian Sharpe, Pete Sherwood, Malcolm Whittaker and Brian Wilson. All other photographs Perceptive Images

Mortons Media Group
Publisher: Dan Savage
Layout and design:
Charlotte Pearson and Justin Blackamore
Production editor: Janet Richardson
Production manager: Craig Lamb

Mortons Media Group Ltd
Media Centre, Morton Way,
Horncastle, Lincolnshire LN9 6JR
Tel 01507 523456

Printed by
William Gibbons and Son,
Wolverhampton

Above: Severn Valley based Stanier Mogul No 2968 heads a demonstration freight train at Garth Y Dwr, during a 2008 visit to the Llangollen Railway. *David Gibson.*

BRITISH STEAM
PRESERVED

There are a very healthy number of working and 'as rescued' steam locomotives based at the 115 or so heritage railway centres of the UK, and a lesser number displayed in museums. The collections are made up of ex British Railways locomotives, ex industrial locomotives, imported locomotives, locomotives withdrawn from service before the formation of BR in 1948 and increasingly 'new build' locomotives. This publication focuses on the locations and condition of the preserved steam locomotives which became British Railways stock at the time of nationalisation and those built thereafter. There are a total of 387 ex 'BR' locomotives operating or awaiting restoration at UK centres.

There are certainly enough steam locos to go around and the types on view broadly represent Britain's railways of yesteryear. In addition to operating on preserved railways, restored steam locomotives work regularly hauling special trains on the UK's national rail network, although for how many years to come and to what extent that practice will continue is the subject of much debate.

British Railways steam locomotive year-on-year stock totals illustrate that the end of steam traction was very much a gradual affair, conducted over 20 years. The number of new locomotives introduced by BR between 1948 and 1960 was a much lower total than those withdrawn from service over the same period. There were some 'false dawns' along the way as in order to cope with changing traffic patterns some locomotive types actually increased in number; however the overall trend was inexorably a downward one.

Figures for the 20 years 1948 to 1967 show that while the activities of the much maligned Dr Richard Beeching (BTC/BR June 1961 to June 1965), certainly gave extra momentum to the process, the withdrawal of steam locomotives was already well under way. The total number of steam locomotives in 1948 was just over 20,000, by 1960 that total had fallen to just over 13,000. The introduction of Diesel Multiple Units and diesel locomotives, together with further electrification over the period, reduced the number of steam locomotives needed to operate the network. Later Beeching's plans would reduce that number further, and additionally shrink the network!

Large freight tonnages were steadily being lost to the 'then' rapidly growing road transport industry. Consider also that the coal to power the steam locomotives was transported by rail.

To get an idea of the coal tonnages moved assume that on average a tank loco tender held three tons (GWR Pannier three ton six cwts) and the average tender loco six tons (LMS Jubilee nine tons). Therefore filling all the tenders of the 1948 stock of 20,000 locomotives would take almost 100,000 tons of coal. On average serviceable locomotives would be coaled at least six times a week, many employed on express services, even twice a day. Those simple figures illustrate that the railway's 'own usage' coal tonnages were truly enormous.

Above: **Proud Centenarians. '9000 Dukedog' 4-4-0 No 9017 Earl of Berkeley, built in 1906, double heads with the record breaking '3440 Class' 4-4-0 No 3440 City of Truro, built in 1903. Pictured at the 2008 SV Gala.** *David Gibson.*

Right: **Billington ex LBSCR 'E4 Class' 0-6-2T No 32473, seen on the Bluebell Railway in BR Southern Region livery.** *Paul Pettitt.*

BR STEAM LOCOMOTIVE STOCK, SELECTED YEAR END TOTALS 1948 – 1967

Type	31/12 1948	31/12 1950	31/12 1952	31/12 1954	31/12 1956	31/12 1958	31/12 1960	31/12 1961	31/12 1962	31/12 1964	31/12 1965	31/12 1966	31/12 1967	Preserved Locomotives
Tender	12800	12293	11783	11599	11333	10740	9156	8265	6391	3939	2582	1572	359	**227**
Tank	7411	7305	7076	6822	6189	5359	4115	3422	2372	1024	402	114	0	**160**
Total	20211	19598	18859	18421	17522	16099	13271	11687	8763	4963	2984	1686	359	**387**

ongoing movement allows us all to appreciate and celebrate the UK's wonderful railway heritage. In particular the enduring attraction of steam power continues to fascinate and provide pleasure for many thousands of people throughout the country. Steam power is alive, well and even growing, thanks to the dedicated preservationists.

Saving steam locomotives from the cutting torch was a big thing in itself but for the most part they were not saved just to be looked at, they were rescued in order that they would steam again. But where would that happen? Fortunately those early day preservationists had the good sense to also save sections of railway no longer wanted as part of the national network. How could they steam again? The majority did not pass into preservation as working engines but as scrapped redundant heavy machinery. Putting a steam locomotive back to work requires a huge amount of

effort, an immeasurable amount of skill and a great deal of money.

It does not of course end there. The first time a fire is lit in a newly restored loco the clock starts ticking as boilers, fireboxes and the like only have an average lifespan of 10 years. Many preserved steam locomotives have been the subject of second rebuilds, indeed some are facing a third major refurbishment. Such is the magical attraction of steam that people who were not even born when steam was banished from BR are now experienced part-time footplate crews and railway engineers, others also too young to clearly remember the infamous Dr Beeching regularly staff some of the stations and signalboxes 'his' plan forced into closure. The development of the UK's Preserved Railways is a fascinating subject in its own right, and one we shall return to on another occasion. First let us look at the 387 rescued ex BR locomotives which form the largest part of Britain's varied and priceless steam locomotive inheritance.

Top: **Stanier 'Princess Coronation' No 6233 Duchess of Sutherland pictured in Crewe Works during the 2005 Great Gathering.**

Above: **Back home! Seen at Crewe Loco Works in 2005 Stanier 'Jubilee 4-6-0 No 5690 Leander (LMS number) with Stanier Mogul (2-6-0) 42968.**

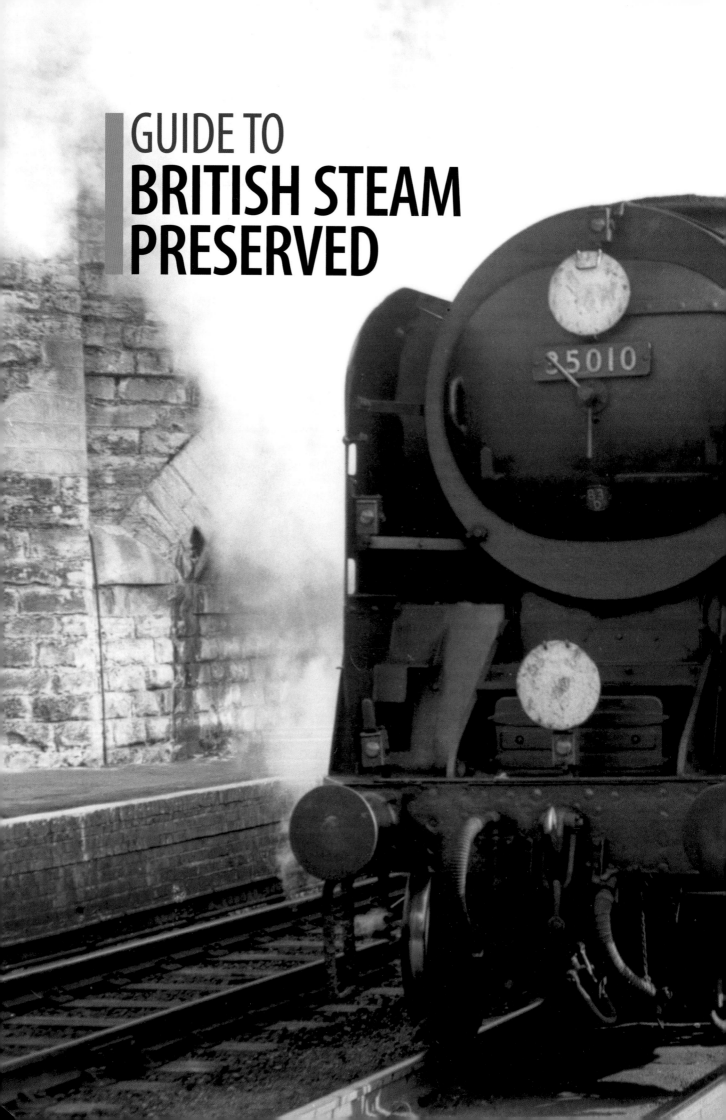

GUIDE TO
BRITISH STEAM
PRESERVED

Rebuilt ex Merchant Navy Pacific 35010 Blue Star is pictured leaving Axminster with an up stopping train to Salisbury from Exeter in the 1960s. *David Anderson*

Preservation can often be a lengthy process and it is always costly! Merchant Navy Pacific 35010 Blue Star was just over 24 years in BR ownership, thereafter 19 years in the Woodhams of Barry scrap line and to date 24 years in preserved ownership. Built in 1942 No 35010 was withdrawn from BR service in 1966 and sold for scrap. It was purchased by the British Engineman's Steam Preservation Society in January 1985 and moved to a private site near the North Woolwich Station Museum. The locomotive owners then moved it to the Colne Valley Railway in 1996. In 2009, 67 years after leaving Eastleigh Works the once magnificent Bullied Pacific is on static display at Colne Valley, awaiting a return to steam!

Number	Name	Class	Type	Ex Work	Builder	Ex BR	Location	Status 2009
7822	Foxcote Manor	7800	4-6-0	1950	Sdn	1965	LR (80)	Operational

Each locomotive is listed either individually or with others of the same class, as shown in the example above.

NUMBERS given are those carried in BR service unless otherwise stated.

NAMES are those carried by the locomotive in BR service at anytime between 1948 and 1968, names given to steam locomotives in preservation are not necessarily shown.

CLASS identification numbers are those 'as listed' in the BR stock lists of the period.

TYPE refers to the wheel arrangement and if applicable style of tank locomotive, eg ST saddle tank, PT pannier tank, WT well tank and T side tank.

EX WORKS refers to the year in which the locomotive was outshopped, and taken into revenue-earning service. If the year is pre-1948 and after 1922 then the locomotive concerned will have been built by, or for, one of the big four companies ie GWR, LMS, LNER and SR. Prior to 1922 the locomotive will have been built by a pre-grouping railway company. Locomotives built 1948 to 1968 are of British Railways origin but could still be to a design originated by one of the aforementioned railway companies, or of BR Standard design.

BUILDER refers, by abbreviations, to the works at which the locomotive was originally built. A table of builders and relevant abbreviations is shown at the end of this section. Includes new build locomotives to BR or pre-nationalisation designs.

EX BR is the year in which the locomotive was taken out of revenue-earning service by BR. In the majority of cases it is not the date the locomotive was cut up or saved for preservation.

LOCATION refers, by abbreviations, to the normal home base of the locomotive. In most cases a number in brackets refers to the railway centre concerned, as detailed in the Preserved Railway Directory on pages 126-129 of this publication. NRM denotes national collection locomotive. Preserved steam locomotives are regularly loaned to other railways for either short periods or whole seasons, additionally they can 'move' following a change of ownership etc. The home base details are to the best of our knowledge correct at the time of going to press. To be sure of a locomotive's present location use the contact information shown on the directory pages.

STATUS refers to the condition of the preserved locomotive (at the time of going to press). Some abbreviations are used and a table is shown at the end of this section.

LOCOMOTIVE WORKS/BUILDERS AND ABBREVIATIONS USED:

AB	Andrew Barclay Sons & Co Ltd	K	Kitson & Co
Asfd	Ashford	KS	Kerr Stuart & Co Ltd
AW	Sir WG Armstrong Whitworth & Co Ltd	Lngh	Longhedge
		LR	Llangollen Railway
Bow	Bow Works	N	Neilson & Co
BP	Beyer Peacock & Co Ltd	NBL	North British Locomotive Co Ltd
Bbel	Bluebell Railway	RS	Robert Stephenson & Co Ltd
Bton	Brighton	RSH	Robert Stephenson & Hawthorns Ltd
Cow	Cowlairs		
Crw	Crewe	S	Sentinel (Shrewsbury) Ltd
Dar	Darlington	S&M	Shropshire & Montgomeryshire Railway
Der	Derby		
Don	Doncaster	Sdn	Swindon
Elh	Eastleigh	SRlx	St Rollox (Glasgow)
ELR	East Lancashire Railway	SS	Sharp Stewart & Co
Few	Fox Walker & Co	Str	Stratford
Ghd	Gateshead	SVR	Severn Valley Railway
Gor	Gorton	V	Vulcan Ironworks (USA)
Hor	Horwich	VF	Vulcan Foundry Ltd
HE	Hunslet Engine Co Ltd	9Elm	Nine Elms
HR	Highland Railway	WSR	West Somerset Railway

LOCOMOTIVE STATUS CATEGORIES:

Operational	Fit for service.
Under repair	A serviceable locomotive, undergoing repairs.
Stored o/u	Has steamed in preservation, but not now stored out of use.
Rebuild	Has steamed in preservation, but now being rebuilt or re-boilered.
Restoration	Being restored, for the first time.
Long term	Very long term restoration project.
Scrap cond	Little or no work has been done since rescue.

35010 still unrestored in 2008.

NEW BOOKS FROM STRATHWOOD

Sixties Spotting Days Around the London Midland Region

Over one hundred and fifty evocative colour photographs across 96 pages, recall the era once more of Duchesses, Jubilees, Scots leading the way before the coming of the diesels and electrics in increased numbers. We visit Crewe sheds and works, the WCML and the Midland routes as we relive again those happy care free days in the sun visiting sheds and sitting by the lineside.

Sixties Spotting Days Around the Southern Region

Covers in some detail the hotspots such as Waterloo, Nine Elms, Clapham Junction, Basingstoke, Eastleigh, Southampton, Bournemouth, Weymouth, the Brighton lines and the cross country routes are also well covered, again with delightful colour shots hitherto unpublished.

Sixties Spotting Days 1968 The Last Year of Steam

We relive the year month by month, taking in again those last steam workings, enthusiast specials, shed visits, withdrawals, scrap yards and take look at what was happening as well with the fast changing diesel and electric scene along with some splendid views of early preservation days, Open Days and the industrial steam some of which was ex BR that caught our attention once we had come to terms with August 1968.

Seventies Spotting Days Around the Western Region

Brings us the last years of the hydraulics, Warships, Westerns, Hymeks, NBL Class 22s, green and blue Class 47s & 37s, the arrival of the Class 50s, Peaks, Blue Pullmans and even Class 40s on railtours all feature along with Paddington, Old Oak Common, Reading, Swindon, Bristol, Exeter, Plymouth and the Devon sea wall stretches.

Seventies Spotting Days Around the London Midland Region

Superb 1970s colour shots as we review the WCML, with features on Crewe, station depot and Works, Woodhead electrics with visits to Reddish and Guide Bridge, the S&C captures our attention in summer and in winter snows. The Midland mainline is not forgotten taking in Toton and Derby. Classes seen include 24s, 25s, 44s, 45s, 20s, 47s, 50s, 76s and ac electrics 81-87.

These are all limited print run titles, 96 pages hardback and on glossy quality paper.

£19.95 each inc P&P within the UK

Also still available
Sixties Spotting Days Around the Eastern Region
and
Two Decades of Scottish Steam
£19.95 each inc P&P within the UK

Payment: Visa/Mastercard/Switch or Sterling cheque drawn on a UK bank. Order via post, telephone or email.
Overseas book orders only, please add 15% for postage

Strathwood (HRW2)

Glenavon House, Kinchurdy Road, Boat of Garten, Inverness-shire PH24 3BP
PRIORITY ORDER HOTLINE: Tel: 01479 831139

EX BR STANDARD
LOCOMOTIVES

When formed by the British Transport Commission in January 1948 British Railways took into stock 20,260 steam locomotives of which five were narrow gauge. The total was made up of a multiplicity of classes and types produced by the four companies amalgamated to form BR, the Great Western Railway, the Southern Railway, the London Midland & Scottish Railway and the London North Eastern Railway; those organisations in 1927 each inherited locomotives from the pre-amalgamation railway companies. Many of the steam locomotives acquired by BR were almost life expired and the vast majority badly maintained due to the difficult working conditions imposed on the railways between 1939 and 1945, the period of WWII.

To correct the balance British Railways decided to embark upon a programme of steam locomotive building from 1951 onwards while at the same time withdrawing from service large numbers of older engines. The production of a new breed of steam locomotives was sanctioned by the BTC even given the advancement of dieselisation and the anticipated proliferation of electric traction. As time has shown, the Standard Classes, although in the main excellent locomotives, were in the long term only a stopgap measure, with various examples in BR service for less than 10 years and others for only five. BR Standards in service peaked at 999 locomotives, a total which had fallen to 792 by the end of 1963 and then to only 52 locomotives as the last year of steam on BR approached.

Standard 9F 2-10-0 No 92203, named Black Prince in preservation, is pictured departing Irwell Vale during a visit to the East Lancashire Railway.

BUILT IN BRITAIN

The total number of steam locomotives in BR stock by the end of 1951 (the year Standard types were first introduced) had fallen to 19,148, as the number scrapped was greater than the number built, a pattern which was set to continue. The 1960 year-end total, which included the 999 Standard locomotives built, amounted to 13,296 steam locomotives. A total of 46 BR Standard types have been preserved and there are three 'new build' projects under way one of which is the conversion of a 2-6-0 tender type to a 2-6-2T tank engine. The preserved ex BR Standard locomotives are listed in numerical order and shown in classes. Standard steam locomotives were listed in a number series from 70000 to 92250.

Within that series were locomotives with numbers 90000 to 90731 and 90750 to 90774 which were Ministry of Supply (War Department) 'Austerity' locomotives which saw service in all regions of BR, none of which survived directly into UK preservation. However others which worked overseas have now been preserved in Britain, together with an example from the Longmoor Military Railway.

Below: **First of the 999 Standards, 70000 Britannia is seen when under construction at Crewe Works.**

BR Standard 'Britannia Class' was the first of the 'Riddles' Standard types to enter service with BR. The first of the class 70000 Britannia was rolled out of Crewe Locomotive Works in January 1951. The new class of 55 engines were considered at the time to be a striking design of Mixed Traffic locomotives, intended to have wide route availability. The Britannias were roughly equal in power to the WR Castle, the LMR Royal Scot, the SR West Country Pacific and the Eastern Region V2.

The 4-6-2 locomotives were designed in the Derby drawing office of BR and all were built at Crewe. They were given the number series 70000 to 70054 with 70000 to 70024 entering service in 1951, 70025 to 70044 entering service in 1952/53 and 70045 to 70054 in 1954. The class was at first distributed around the network with 15 engines going to the Eastern Region, five to the Western Region, 15 to the London Midland Region and five to the Scottish Region. Thereafter some changes in allocation were made which meant that three engines went to the Southern Region and additional engines from the LMR allocation going to the Eastern.

The Britannia's design was generally considered to be a complete success and when first in service the type put in some memorable performances on the former Great Eastern Railway main line into East Anglia, as a result of which timings were appreciably improved. As dieselisation (and later electrification) became more advanced all of the Britannias were transferred to the London Midland Region. The first to be scrapped was 70007 Coeur-de-Lion which was cut up at Crewe in July 1965, having worked in BR service for only 14 years. By 1966 just 42 of the class were still in use.

Originally BR intended to preserve 70000 Britannia as part of the national collection but then dropped that plan following vandalism of the class leader while it was stored in their care. The British Railways Board alternatively chose 70013 Oliver Cromwell for the collection, as a result of which the loco was overhauled and repainted at Crewe Works in January 1967, prior to preservation. The engine was then returned to traffic hauling special trains right up to the end of steam on BR, including the final leg of a Farewell to Steam special from Manchester to Carlisle on 11 August 1968. Number 70000 Britannia was eventually preserved after being privately purchased. Both locomotives should be actively involved on preserved services in the near future as 70013 returned to steam in 2008 and 70000 is expected to be outshopped in 2009 after an extensive rebuild. Power Classification 7P6F/7MT. Driving Wheel 6ft 2in, Cylinders outside.

Number	Name	Class	Type	Ex Works	Builder	Ex BR	Location	Status 2009
70000	Britannia	Brit	4-6-2	1951	Crw	1966	L&NWR	Rebuild
70013	Oliver Cromwell	Brit	4-6-2	1951	Crw	1968	NRM/Tours	Operational

Standard Britannia number 70000 is pictured at Wolvercot Junction in 1963 with an Oxford (Cowley)-Birmingham (Longbridge) car transporter train.
David Anderson.

Britannia hurries an express freight south through Watford Junction Station in 1964.

Oliver Cromwell returned to the main line after a major overhaul in the summer of 2008 in order to commemorate the end of steam on BR. *Fred Kerr.*

Oliver Cromwell is pictured at Stockport waiting to work a main line special on 28 April 1968.

The engine crew give Britannia Pacific 4-6-2 70013 Oliver Cromwell a last look over before working an end of steam special run.

Above: Standard Class Britannia Pacific 4-6-2 70000 is pictured approaching Calverley with a Holyhead-Crewe working just prior to being retired pending a rebuild.

BR Standard 'Duke of Gloucester Class' the 4-6-2 Pacific locomotive number 71000 and named Duke of Gloucester was the only example of the design built. It was constructed at Crewe Works and entered traffic in 1954. Building the big locomotive had been authorised following the destruction of 46202 Princess Anne in the Harrow & Wealdstone crash of 1952. It was a prototype of an intended class of main line locomotives, which in the event were never built.

The Riddles designed loco was built with Caprotti* valve gear and as a three-cylinder engine it was more powerful than the Britannias. Heralded as the ultimate British steam locomotive design, 71000 failed to deliver the performances which the builders had envisaged. As the railway modernisation plan was well under way BR never put in the time and effort which may have solved the engine's performance problems. It was withdrawn in November 1962 and after the cylinders and motion were removed in an act of partial preservation, the loco was sent to a Barry scrapyard to be cut up.

Fortunately the unique locomotive was saved by a group of dedicated preservationists and has since run many times on the main line and at preserved railways. The preservation group invested time and money on the 'Duke' solving all of its previously reported

problems, after which they rightly claimed that during the first years of the new millennium 71000 did become worthy of the accolade 'ultimate steam locomotive'. The powerful Standard 'Class 8' has steamed considerably longer in private ownership than it did for BR. Power Classification 8P. Driving Wheel 6ft 2in, Cylinders three.

*The majority of British steam locomotives were fitted with either Stephenson of Walschaerts valve gear which controlled the flow of steam to and from the cylinders, they are operated by a series of cranks and levers acting on conventional piston valves. Caprotti valve gear is very different as it uses cam actuated Poppet valves, similar to an internal combustion engine to control the steam flows to and from the locomotive's cylinders. The cams are operated by an easily discernable rotary shaft driven by a worm gear mounted on a return crank fixed to the centre driving wheel.

The Caprotti valve gear is named after its inventor the Italian engineer Arturo Caprotti. During the 1950s an improved version was developed in the UK thus 'British Caprotti valve gear' was fitted to the last two British Railways-built 'Black Fives' 44686/7, the last 30 BR standard class 5s, numbers 73125-54 and of course 71000.

The rotary shaft which actuates the Standard 8 locomotive's Caprotti valve gear cams is clearly visable.

Number	Name	Class	Type	Ex Work	Builder	Ex BR	Location	Status 2009
71000	Duke of Gloucester	Duke	4-6-2	1954	Crw	1962	ELR (109)	Operational

Preserved

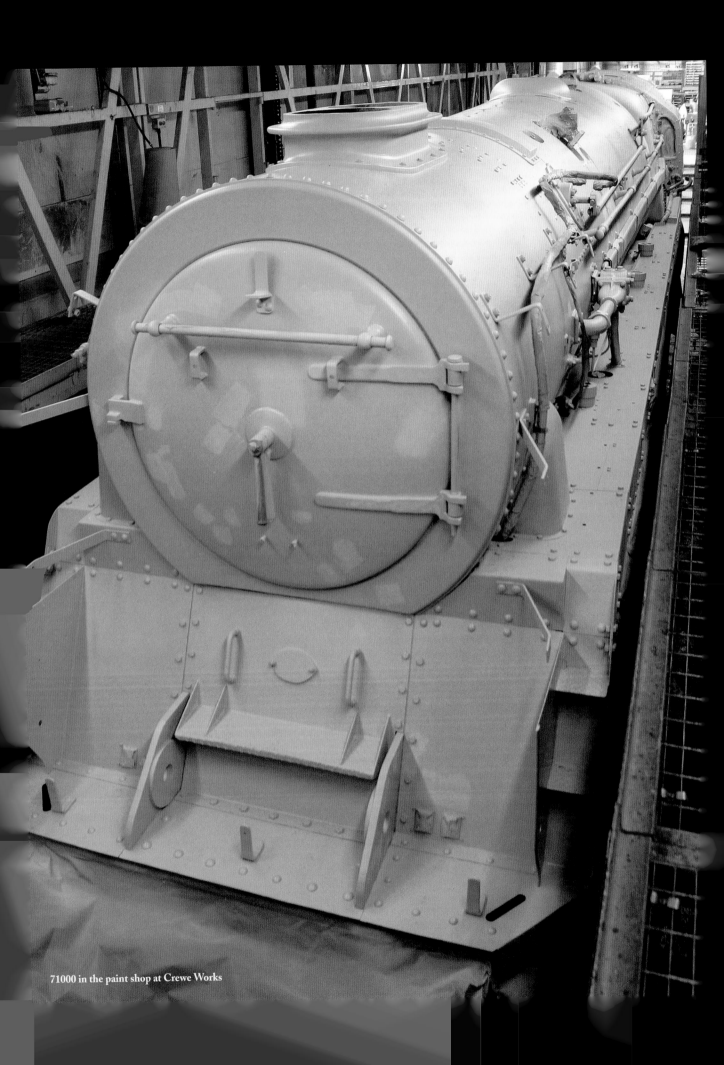

71000 in the paint shop at Crewe Works

71000 Duke of Gloucester returned to Crewe Works in July 2004 and as part of a major overhaul before returning to main line duty 'she' received a new high quality paint job. The work was carried out under contract by Bombardier Ltd and funded by 'a friend' of the locomotive. 71000 is seen in primer in the paint shop and as finished displaying the famous 'Phoenix' headboard.

No 71000 Duke of Gloucester racing through Winsford on the WCML, heading for London Euston with a BBC Radio Merseyside 'Children in Need'

No 71000 Duke of Gloucester is pictured leaving Irwell Vale on the East Lancashire Railway while 'running in' after a rebuild; note the two patches of

BR Standard 'Class 5' 4-6-0 types were produced between 1951 and 1957 and the 172 locomotives given the number series 73000 to 73171; they were a 'Riddles' Doncaster design. The design was based on the LMS type 'Black Fives' and they were intended to replace that class, the LNER type B1s, the GWR type Halls and the SR type King Arthur Class.

The Class 5s were sent to all regions of BR and 20 of the SR allocation were given the names of the 'King Arthurs' they replaced. In line with all the Standard types which followed, they were successful engines, incorporating cut-away tender sides to improve vision when running tender first. The Standards were easier to maintain and service, being fitted with newly designed standard self-cleaning features.

All of the class were built with the, by then, standard high running plate and additionally locomotives 73125-54 were fitted with Caprotti valve gear. British Railways built 172 of this type between 1951 and 1957 mainly at Derby; however 42 of the class were built at Doncaster. Power Classification 5MT. Driving Wheel 6ft 2in, Cylinders outside.

BR Standard 'Class 5' 4-6-0 No 73082 Camelot, a loco which has run in preservation and is based at the Bluebell Railway, is pictured in 1960s BR service at Didcot shed. The small nameplate can just be seen on the running plate above the centre wheel. *David Anderson.*

Number	Name	Class	Type	Ex Work	Builder	Ex BR	Location	Status 2009
73050		Stan 5	4-6-0	1954	Der	1968	NVR (68)	Rebuild
73082	Camelot	Stan 5	4-6-0	1955	Der	1966	Bbell (2)	Rebuild
73096		Stan 5	4-6-0	1955	Der	1967	MHants (11)	Operational
73129		Stan 5	4-6-0	1956	Der	1967	MRC (50)	Operational
73156		Stan 5	4-6-0	1956	Don	1967	GCR (49)	Restoration

BR Standard 'Class 4' 4-6-0 No 75069 is based at the Severn Valley Railway, the Swindon-built loco makes a fine sight during a 1990 'Cambrian Limited' mainline working.

BR Standard 'Class 4' 4-6-0 types were introduced between 1952 and 1957 and carried the number series 75000 to 75079. They were constructed to a 'Riddles' Brighton design and all built at Swindon. The first entered service in May 1951 and the last examples left the works in June 1957. They were a smaller and lighter version of the '73000 Class', and therefore enjoyed almost universal route availability.

They were originally allocated to the Western Region where they were especially popular on the routes of the former Cambrian Railways, the London Midland Region, and the Southern Region. A further batch of 10 engines was to have been built for use on the Eastern Region, but the steady march of dieselisation caused that order to be cancelled. From 1957 onwards 21 of the class were fitted with double chimneys. Power Classification 4MT. Driving Wheel 5ft 8in, cylinders outside.

Number	Name	Class	Type	Ex Work	Builder	Ex BR	Location	Status 2009
75014		Stan 4	4-6-0	1951	Sdn	1966	Pa/Dart (33)	Operational
75027		Stan 4	4-6-0	1954	Sdn	1968	Bbell (2)	Stored o/u
75029		Stan 4	4-6-0	1954	Sdn	1967	NYMR (99)	Operational
75069		Stan 4	4-6-0	1955	Sdn	1966	SVR (59)	Stored o/u
75078		Stan 4	4-6-0	1956	Sdn	1966	K&WVR (95)	Rebuild
75079		Stan 4	4-6-0	1956	Sdn	1966	MHants (11)	Restoration

'Mogul' 'Class 4' 2-6-0 No 76017 is preserved at the Mid-Hants Railway, the loco is pictured in BR service while shunting at Axminster. *David Anderson.*

BR Standard 'Mogul' 'Class 4' 2-6-0 No 76079 heads a pair of ex LMS Ivatt Moguls through Hampton Loade Station during an SVR gala event.

BR Standard 'Class 4' 2-6-0 types were 'Riddles' Doncaster-designed 4MT Moguls (2-6-0 tender locos) with the number series 76000 to 76114. The total build number was 115 locomotives which entered service between 1952 and 1957, 45 were built at Horwich and 70 at Doncaster. The type was based on the earlier Ivatt '43000 Class' 2-6-0s (built for the LMS and BR) and in common with that type they were intended for cross country work and were used successfully on a wide variety of duties, and were popular with engine crews and maintenance personnel. The class were allocated to all BR regions except the Western Region. Power Classification 4MT. Driving Wheel 5ft 3in, Cylinders outside.

Number	Name	Class	Type	Ex Work	Builder	Ex BR	Location	Status 2009
76017		Stan 4	2-6-0	1953	Hor	1965	MHants (11)	Stored o/u
76077		Stan 4	2-6-0	1956	Hor	1967	G&WR (48)	Rebuild
76079		Stan 4	2-6-0	1957	Hor	1967	ELR (109) Tours	Operational
76084		Stan 4	2-6-0	1957	Hor	1967	NYMR (99) Private site Morpeth	Restoration

BR Standard 'Class 2' The 'Riddles' Derby-designed 'Standard Class 2' 2MT 2-6-0 (Mogul) type with the number series 78000 to 78064 were similar in design to the Ivatt LMS 4MT '46400' types. All 65 of this very popular class, designed for light passenger work, were built at Darlington Works between 1952 and 1956. Power Classification 2 MT. Driving Wheel 5ft, Cylinders outside.

Right: BR Standard 'Class 2' 2MT 2-6-0 (Mogul) No 78022 is pictured in BR service at Preston in 1964. This locomotive is based at the Keighley & Worth Valley Railway.

Number	Name	Class	Type	Ex Work	Builder	Ex BR	Location	Status 2009
78018		Stan 2	2-6-0	1954	Dar	1966	Darlington Rly Centre	Restoration
78019		Stan 2	2-6-0	1954	Dar	1966	GCR (49)	Restoration
78022		Stan 2	2-6-0	1954	Dar	1966	K&WVR (95)	Rebuild
78059*		Stan 2	2-6-0	1956	Dar	1966	Bbell (2)	N/A

*Donor for 'New Build' 84030 2-6-2T 'Standard Class 2 Tank' project.

BR Standard 'Class 4 Tank' the '80000' series tanks were the first of three Riddles Standard tank locomotive types, they carried the number series 80000 to 80154. The 'Class 4' 4MT 2-6-4T was a highly successful design which when allocated to all regions of BR (except the Western) found universal favour with engine crews. There were 155 built between 1951 and 1957. The Brighton design incorporated the same 'BR5' boiler as the Standard 4MT tender engines. Only 25 of these locomotives lasted until 1966 and none made it past the end of 1967.

The class was intended for use on suburban passenger and semi-fast services. Built at Derby 15 locos, Doncaster 10 locos, and Brighton 130 locos they were based on the earlier Stanier/Fairburn 2-6-4T '42500' series of LMS tank engines. They had a good turn of speed and great powers of acceleration making then eminently suitable for suburban passenger work, and very popular with footplate crews. Power Classification 4MT. Driving Wheel 5ft 8in, Cylinders outside.

Bluebell Railway Standard 'Class 4' tank No 80064 is pictured hard at work for BR in the 1960 near Axminster, with an up freight. *David Anderson.*

Standard 'Class 4' 2-6-4 tank No 80002, which is preserved at the Keighley & Worth Valley Railway, is pictured while in BR service at Polmadie Motive Power Depot, Glasgow in 1956. *David Anderson.*

Standard Tanks in Snowdonia. 80079 and 80098 pictured on the single line between Betws-y-Coed and Blaenau Ffestiniog.

Severn Valley-based 'Standard 4' tank No 80079 is seen leaving Hampton Loade with a demonstration freight working for Kidderminster.

Number	Name	Class	Type	Ex Work	Builder	Ex BR	Location	Status 2009
80002		Stan 4T	2-6-4T	1952	Der	1967	K&WVR (95)	Operational
80064		Stan 4T	2-6-4T	1953	Bton	1965	Bbell (2)	Static display
80072		Stan 4T	2-6-4T	1954	Bton	1965	LR (80)	Restoration
80078		Stan 4T	2-6-4T	1954	Bton	1965	Swang (37)	Operational
80079		Stan 4T	2-6-4T	1954	Bton	1965	SVR (59)	Static display
80080		Stan 4T	2-6-4T	1954	Bton	1965	MRC (50)	Rebuild
80097		Stan 4T	2-6-4T	1954	Bton	1965	ELR(109)	Restoration
80098		Stan 4T	2-6-4T	1954	Bton	1965	MRC (50) Tours	Operational
80100		Stan 4T	2-6-4T	1955	Bton	1965	Bbell (2)	Scrap cond
80104		Stan 4T	2-6-4T	1955	Bton	1965	Swang (37)	Operational
80105		Stan 4T	2-6-4T	1955	Bton	1965	Bness (103)	Operational
80135		Stan 4T	2-6-4T	1956	Bton	1965	NYMR (99)	Stored o/u
80136		Stan 4T	2-6-4T	1956	Bton	1965	LNWR	Rebuild
80150		Stan 4T	2-6-4T	1956	Bton	1965	Barry (72)	Scrap cond
80151		Stan 4T	2-6-4T	1957	Bton	1967	Bbell (2)	Operational

BR 'Standard Class 9' was by far the most powerful, and many would argue the most successful 'Riddles' BR Standard type; they carried the number series 92000 to 92250. The immensely powerful 2-10-0 freight locomotives were designed at Brighton. The total built between 1954 and 1960 was 251 engines, 198 at Crewe and 53 at Swindon. Engine number 92220 holds the distinction of being the last steam locomotive built by British Railways, painted in lined green livery and given a GWR-style copper topped chimney it was rolled out of Swindon Works in March 1960, and to mark the occasion was named 'Evening Star'.

This impressive class had only a short service life, but long enough to prove their worth. The original design 9F 2-10-0s were powerful, reliable and popular with the engine crews. The 21ft 8in wheelbase had to be capable of following tight curves and, to achieve this, the BR Standard team designed the centre pair of driving wheels without flanges, and to widen route availability kept the axle loading to only 15 tons 10cwt. The locomotives were designed for use on the heaviest of freight trains at reasonably high speeds. In service they also worked passenger trains at speeds reported to be between 80 and 90mph, an incredible achievement for an engine with only 5ft diameter driving wheels. Real pulling power was the main asset of the Standard Class 9s. With great success they worked heavy, mineral, coal and general freight trains. The Tyne Dock to Consett workings were perhaps the hardest regular tasks ever undertaken by the class, and those iron ore trains could weigh up to 787 tons each. In addition they had to be hauled up gradients as steep as 1 in 35, a task that proved well within the capabilities of 9Fs working in pairs. Ten examples 92060-92066 and 92097-92099 were fitted with Westinghouse air pumps in order to work the hopper doors on the mineral trains. Power Classification 9F. Driving Wheel 5ft, Cylinders outside.

Below: **Not a Prince! BR Standard 9F 2-10-0 No 9220 seen in BR service at Foxhall Junction, Didcot West Curve with a Swindon-Birmingham freight.** *David Anderson.*

Bottom: **Now a Prince! Preserved BR Standard 9F N 92203 pictured during a visit the East Lancashire Railway. The loco received the name Black Prince in preservation.**

Above: **Standard 9F No 92245 is pictured in BR service with a Birmingham-Swindon freight. This loco is based at Barry but was still in scrap condition in 2008 some 44 years since being withdrawn from service.**
David Anderson.

Left: **Engine No 92220 holds the distinction of being the last steam locomotive built by British Railways; painted in lined green livery and given a GWR-style copper topped chimney it was rolled out of Swindon Works in March 1960, and to mark the occasion was named 'Evening Star'. Pictured near Chester in May 1982.**

Number	Name	Class	Type	Ex Work	Builder	Ex BR	Location	Status 2009
92134		Stan 9	2-10-0	1957	Crw	1966	L&NWR	Restoration
92203	Black Prince*	Stan 9	2-10-0	1959	Sdn	1967	G&WR (48)	Operational
92207	Morning Star*	Stan 9	2-10-0	1959	Sdn	1964	Shillingstone Station	Restoration
92212		Stan 9	2-10-0	1959	Sdn	1968	MHants (11)	Restoration
92214		Stan 9	2-10-0	1959	Sdn	1965	MRC (50)	Operational
92219		Stan 9	2-10-0	1960	Sdn	1965	MRC (50)	Operational
92220	Evening Star	Stan 9	2-10-0	1960	Sdn	1965	NRM Steam Swindon	Static display
92240		Stan 9	2-10-0	1958	Crw	1965	Bbell (2)	Static display
92245		Stan 9	2-10-0	1958	Crw	1964	Barry (72)	Scrap cond

*Name given in preservation

NEW BUILDS
WORK IN PROGRESS

72010 Hengist

Between 1951 and 1952 ten lighter versions of the Britannia class were constructed, the Standard 'Class 6' 6MT 4-6-2 Clans. However the Crewe-built small Pacifics were not as successful as their bigger cousins and that fact coupled with the quickening pace of dieselisation caused an order for a further fifteen to be cancelled. All of the class were allocated to the Scottish Region and worked mainly on Glasgow-Manchester/Liverpool express services. Locomotives numbered 72000-72004 were taken out of service in 1962, numbers 72005, 72007 and 72009 in 1965 while 72006 and 72008 lasted until 1966. None were preserved. However there is an ongoing project to build an example of the type which will carry the number 72010 and be named Hengist. The project was originated at the Swanage Railway.

Right: **No BR Standard 'Clan' 6MT 4-6-2 made it into preservation but a group based at the Swanage Railway plan to create one. Pictured is No 72004 Clan Macdonald on Beattock Bank in 1959 with a Carlisle-Glasgow Central four-coach stopping train.** *David Anderson.*

Number	Name	Class	Type	Start Date	Builder	Donor loco	Location	Status 2009
72010	Hengist	Clan	4-6-2	2006	Hengist 2007 Society		Swan (37)	Ongoing

Locomotive 82045

The 82045 Locomotive Fund is in the process of building the next member of the extinct Riddles 3MT 2-6-2 82000 tank class, a new loco which is intended specifically for heritage line use. The driving force behind the 82045 project is the conviction that the days of working steam are numbered without an initiative of this kind: even the most recently built of existing BR Standard locomotives are now all but 50 years old, with all the attendant problems of maintenance and repair that this will increasingly cause their owners. It has been suggested that this type could be an ideal candidate for limited series production claiming that batch production would drastically reduce the unit cost of building new 82000s, estimated (2007) at between £1,250,000 and £1,500,000 for 82045.

Left: **A group based at the Severn Valley Railway plan to create a representative of the extinct Riddles 3MT 2-6-2 82000 tank class. 2-6-2T No 82041 is pictured on shed at Bath in 1963.**

Number	Name	Class	Type	Start Date	Builder	Donor loco	Location	Status 2009
82045		Stan3T	2-6-2T	2006	82045 Loco Fund		SVR (59)	Ongoing

Locomotive 84030

Thirty examples of the British Railways Standard Class 2MT 2-6-2 Tank locomotive were built; 84000-84019 at Crewe Works in 1953 and 84020-84029 at Darlington Works in 1957. The first 20 were designed for use on the London Midland Region, while the 10 Darlington-built engines were delivered to the Southern Region. The locos were a slightly heavier BR version of the similar 2MT Tank locomotive designed by Ivatt for the LMS. The last surviving member of the class was sold by BR for scrap in September 1966. Using BR Standard Class 2MT 2-6-0 tender locomotive No 78059 as a donor loco a group based at the Bluebell Railway has embarked upon the process of creating a 2-6-2T.

Using BR Standard Class 2MT 2-6-0 tender locomotive No 78059 as a donor loco, a group based at the Bluebell Railway has embarked upon the process of creating a Standard 2MT 2-6-2T. Class member 84026 is pictured on shunting duties at Stockport in 1965.

Number	Name	Class	Type	Start Date	Builder	Donor loco	Location	Status 2009
84030		Stan2T	2-6-2T		Bluebell Rly Trust	78059	Bbell (2)	Ongoing

Ex Ministry of Supply (WD) Austerity Locomotives

In September 1939 RA Riddles was appointed to the newly created position of Director of Transportation Equipment for the Ministry of Supply, on the very day that war broke out between Britain and Germany. He was given the brief to build a large numbers of locomotives to help the war effort while being mindful of the impending scarcity of raw material and resources.

Between 1943 and 1946 a total of 935 WD 2-8-0 MOD (WD) 'Austerity' locomotives were built by North British Locomotive Co Ltd and Vulcan Foundry Ltd. Many saw service in France, Belgium and Holland during WWII. From delivery until October 1944 all the 2-8-0s in service were 'loaned' by the WD to the UK railway companies but starting in November of that year WD 8F locomotives were gradually shipped overseas.

There was, in 1943, a bigger version of the WD Austerity 8F built by the North British Locomotive Company, with a 2-10-0 wheel arrangement. That class of 150 locomotives were given the extra set of wheels in order to allow them to work over lighter laid track. One of the MOD WD 'Austerity' 8F class 2-10-0s (WD number 73755) had the distinction of being the 1000th WD loco built in the UK.

Right: **Moving under its own steam for the first time in British preservation WD 2-8-0 No 90733 is pictures at L&NWR Heritage Crewe in 2007.**

Locomotive 90733

This locomotive was built in 1945 by Vulcan Foundry at Newton-le-Willows, works number 5200 and was sent to the Netherlands State Railways. In 1953 it was sold to Statens Jarnvagar (SJ – Swedish State Railways) and in 1958 the loco then as No. 1931 was withdrawn from service and stored under cover.

A group of Keighley & Worth Valley Railway members found the loco in an isolated clearing in Sweden and it returned to England on 12 January 1973. Since 1990 KWVR members worked hard restoring the locomotive which steamed again (this time in the UK) in 2007.

There was never a No 90733, it is numbered as the 734th example to work in Britain since WWII.

Number	Name	Class	Type	Ex works	Builder	Rescued	Location	Status 2009
90733*		WD	2-8-0	1945	VF	1976	K&WVR(95)	Operational

*Not a BR number

Locomotive 600 Gordon

Longmoor Military Railway Austerity 2-10-0 number 600 Gordon was built by the North British Locomotiv Co in 1943. This loco was the second engine to emerge out of a class which eventually numbered 150 engines. The locomotive was named in honour of the Royal Engineers' most famous General, Charles Gordon (Gordon of Khartoum). After the war it was used by the Royal Engineers on the Longmoor Military Railway in Hampshire, UK. When the LMR closed in 1969, it was preserved on the Severn Valley Railway. On 25 July 2008 number 600 was formally handed over by the Army to the Severn Valley Railway, who had previously been looking after it in a caretaker capacity.

Left: LMR WD 2-10-0 No 600 Gordon was formally handed over by the Army to the Severn Valley Railway in 2008. The Riddles 2-10-0 is pictured with a demonstration freight train at the SVR in 1984.

Number	Name	Class	Type	Ex works	Builder	Rescued	Location	Status 2009
600*	Gordon	WD	2-10-0	1943	NBL	1969	SVR (59)	Stored o/u

*Longmore number, WD number 73651

Locomotive 73672 Dame Vera Lynn

The Riddles 2-10-0 was built by the North British Locomotive Company, in 1944 for use by the British Army. Within a few months of construction it was numbered 73672 and shipped to Egypt with 15 others where it was placed in store. By October 1945 the 16 locomotives were declared surplus to requirements and sold to the Hellenic State Railways of Greece, being shipped to Salonika in January 1946. 73672 was renumbered Lb960 and based in the Salonika division where it was used on main line passenger duties, including the Athens to Istanbul Express, until withdrawn from service in 1979. It was purchased by a preservation group and shipped to the UK arriving at the Mid Hants Railway in 1984. It was renumbered 3672 and commissioned on 6 August, 1985 by the eminent Dame herself. The locomotive moved to the North Yorkshire Moors Railway in December 1986.

Number	Name	Class	Type	Ex works	Builder	Rescued	Location	Status 2009
3672*	Dame Vera Lynn	WD	2-10-0	1944	NBL	1979	NYMR (99)	Rebuild

*WD number 73672, name given in preservation.

Locomotive 90775

The Riddles-designed WD 2-10-0 90775 was built in 1943 and was the third in the first batch of 100 built by the North British Locomotive Co, carrying works No 25438. It was numbered 3652 by the Ministry of Supply and later, after shipping abroad, was renumbered as WD73652. It was shipped (from new) to Egypt where it worked until 1945. In 1945, along with 15 sister locos it was sold to Hellenic State Railways (SEK). In 1967, having been displaced by new diesels, it was relegated to secondary work and finally withdrawn from service in 1979. It was repatriated to the UK in August 1984. 90775 is now owned by the Midland and Great Northern Joint Railway Society and is based on the North Norfolk Railway.

Number	Name	Class	Type	Ex works	Builder	Rescued	Location	Status 2009
90775*		WD	2-10-0	1943	NBL	1984	NNR (69)	Rebuild

*WD number 73652

EX BR GWR
LOCOMOTIVES

I n 1948 the Western Region of the newly formed British Railways took into stock 3856 locomotives of Great Western Railway origin. By the end of 1960 the Western Region total of operational steam locomotives was 2613; in 1963 the total had reduced to 1276. By the end of 1966 the region's total of standard gauge steam locomotives in regular service was nil.

Preserved ex BR Western Region (GWR) locomotives total 138 examples; it is by far the biggest total of rescued steam engines from any of the pre-nationalisation railway companies. In addition there are currently three GWR-design 'new build' projects under way, utilising other preserved locomotives as 'donors'. One ex GWR 'Class 5101' 2-6-2T locomotive has been rebuilt as a 2-6-0 tender engine.

The preserved locomotives are listed in 'Class' numerical order. The Western Region continued with the GWR four-digit numbering system (numbers between 1000 and 9799). Power Classifications graded 0-9, F refers to freight locomotives, P passenger locomotives, MT mixed traffic locomotives.

Ex GWR Modified Hall 4-6-0 6990 Witherslack Hall is pictured at Didcot in BR WR service. *David Anderson.*

'1338 Class'. Two locomotives were built for the Cardiff Railways one of which was withdrawn and scrapped in 1932. Loco 1338 served British Railways and finished its days shunting at Bridgwater Docks. No coal bunkers were fitted to these engines, a small amount of fuel being carried on the footplate. Power Classification 0F, Driving Wheel 3ft 2½in, Cylinders outside.

Left: **1338 0-4-0ST was designed by Kitson for the Cardiff Railway Co in 1890; the loco is pictured in 1958 at Bridgewater Docks.**

Number	Name	Class	Type	Ex Work	Builder	Ex BR	Location	Status 2009
1338		1338	0-4-0ST	1898	K	1963	Didcot (19)	Operational

'1361 Class', number series 1361-1365 and **'1366 Class'** 1366-1371. These engines were derived from classes originally built for the Cornwall Mineral Railway, but fitted with outside cylinders. They were used primarily for shunting sidings with tight curves. The Class 1363 locos were the last saddle tanks to be built at Swindon Works and were a Churchward design, while the Class 1366 locos (a development of the 1361s) were built with Belpaire boilers and pannier tanks to a Collett design. Power Classifications, 1363 0F and 1369 1F, Driving Wheel both locos 3ft 8in, Cylinders outside both locos.

GWR outside cylinder 0-6-0 Pannier Tank pictured in 1958.

Number	Name	Class	Type	Ex Work	Builder	Ex BR	Location	Status 2009
1363		1361	0-6-0ST	1910	Sdn	1962	Didcot (19)	Static display. Stored o/u

Number	Name	Class	Type	Ex Work	Builder	Ex BR	Location	Status 2009
1369		1366	0-6-0PT	1934	Sdn	1964	SDR(36)	Operational

Above: **In steadily falling rain Collett 0-4-2T 1450 crosses Berwyn Viaduct on the Llangollen Railway with an 'Auto Train' working.**

Left: **'1400 Class' 0-4-2T loco 1466 is pictured as a BR locomotive 'on shed' at Newton Abbot in 1958.**

1400 Class' was originally Class 4800 with the number series 4800-4874; after reclassification in 1946 they were renumbered 1400-1474. BR inherited 75 of the Collett-designed 0-4-2T locomotives which were 'motor fitted' for working push-pull trains. They were used on branch trains over most of the GWR system and were withdrawn from the 1950s onward when diesel railcars were introduced. Power Classification 1P, Driving Wheel 5ft 2in, Cylinders inside.

Right: **'1400 Class' 0-4-2T loco 1466 is pictured as a preserved locomotive.**

Number	Name	Class	Type	Ex Works	Builder	Ex BR	Location	Status 2009
1420		1400	0-4-2T	1933	Sdn	1964	SDR (36)	Operational
1442		1400	0-4-2T	1935	Sdn	1965	Tiverton Museum	Static display
1450		1400	0-4-2T	1935	Sdn	1965	Tours	Operational
1466		1400	0-4-2T	1936	Sdn	1963	Didcot (19)	Static display.

1450 makes a fine sight pictured alongside the restored signalbox at Cheddleton on the Churnet Valley Railway.

'**1500 Class**' of 10 locomotives (1500-1509) all produced to a Hawksworth design under BR. The powerful Pannier Tanks were based in South Wales and London. Three of the class 1501,

1502 and 1509 were sold 'out of service' to the National Coal Board by BR, in 1961. Power Classification 4F, Driving Wheel 4ft 7½in, Cylinders outside.

'1500 Class' loco 1501 pictured on the Severn Valley Railway approaching Hampton Loade with a train ex Kidderminster.

Number	Name	Class	Type	Ex Work	Builder	Ex BR	Location	Status 2009
1501		1500	0-6-0PT	1949	Sdn	NCB 1970	SVR (59)	Static display Stored o/u

'**1600 Class**' locomotives were built under BR to a Hawksworth design number series 1600-1669. Interestingly two engines from the 70-strong class were transferred way out of GWR territory in 1947

when 1646 and 1649 went to Dornoch in Scotland to replace two withdrawn ex Highland Railway tank locos. Power Classification 2F, Driving Wheel 4ft 1½in, Cylinders inside.

Number	Name	Class	Type	Ex Work	Builder	Ex BR	Location	Status 2009
1638		1600	0-6-0PT	1951	Sdn	1966	K&ESR(9)	Operational

'**2301 Class**' engines were commonly referred to as Dean Goods, number series 2322-2579. Many of the once 280-strong class saw

military service during both world wars. Power Classification 2MT, Driving Wheel 5ft 2in, Cylinders inside.

Number	Name	Class	Type	Ex Work	Builder	Ex BR	Location	Status 2009
2516		2301	0-6-0	1897	Sdn	1956	NRM Steam Swindon	Static display

Number	Name	Class	Type	Ex Work	Builder	Ex BR	Location	Status 2009
2807		2800	2-8-0	1905	Sdn	1963	G&WR (48)	Restoration Steam 2009
2818		2800	2-8-0	1905	Sdn	1963	NRM	Static display
2857		2800	2-8-0	1918	Sdn	1963	SVR (59)	Rebuild
2859		2800	2-8-0	1918	Sdn	1964	LR (80)	Scrap cond.
2861		2800	2-8-0	1918	Sdn	1963	Barry (72)	Scrap cond.
2873*		2800	2-8-0	1918	Sdn	1964	SDR (36)	Scrap cond.
2874		2800	2-8-0	1918	Sdn	1963	WSR (39)	Scrap cond.

*Currently donor loco for the restoration of 3803.

'2800 Class' 2-8-0 2857 as a preserved locomotive at the Severn Valley Railway in 1985.

'2800 Class' was a Churchward design of heavy freight locomotives, number series 2800-2883. This was the first 2-8-0 freight locomotive design to be built in the UK. Together with the similar 'Class 2884' they were the GWR's standard freight loco and handled the heaviest trains. During the 1946 coal crisis 12 of the class were modified to oil burning and renumbered in the 4800 series, they were re converted – back to coal burning and re-given their old numbers between 1947-49. Power Classification 8F, Driving Wheel 4ft 7½in, Cylinders outside.

'2884 Class' was a Collett design, number series 2884-2899, 3800-3866. The class is basically a modification of the 'Class 2800' 2-8-0 freight locomotives. During the 1946 coal crisis eight of the class were modified to oil burning and renumbered in the 4850 series, they were reconverted – back to coal burning and re-given their old numbers between 1947-49. They are marginally heavier locomotives with distinctive large side-windowed cabs. Power Classification 8F, Driving Wheels 4ft 7½in, Cylinders outside.

Number	Name	Class	Type	Ex Works	Builder	Ex BR	Location	Status 2009
2885		2884	2-8-0	1938	Sdn	1964	Moor St Sta B-ham	Static display
3802		2884	2-8-0	1938	Sdn	1965	WSR (39)	Operational
3803		2884	2-8-0	1939	Sdn	1963	SDR (36)	Long term
3814		2884	2-8-0	1940	Sdn	1964	NYMR (99)	Long term
3822		2884	2-8-0	1940	Sdn	1964	Didcot (19)	Operational
3845		2884	2-8-0	1942	Sdn	1964	SwiCric (38)	Long term
3850		2884	2-8-0	1942	Sdn	1965	WSR (39)	Operational
3855		2884	2-8-0	1942	Sdn	1965	ELR (109)	Long term
3862		2884	2-8-0	1942	Sdn	1965	Nrt&Lmp(53)	Long term

'2800 Class' 2-8-0 2857 in BR service pictured on an 'up' freight train at Foxhall Junction Didcot. *David Anderson.*

As rescued! '2800 Class' 2874 stands with '2884 Class' 3855 at the Pontypool & Blaenavon Railway in 2003. Both locomotives are now the subject of long term restoration projects, 2874 at the West Somerset Railway and 3855 at the East Lancashire Railway.

'2251 Class' was a Collett-design mixed traffic class, number series 2200-2299, 3200-3219. Locomotive number 3218 from this 120-strong class was the first steam locomotive to be built at Swindon under British Railways management, outshopped in January 1948. Power Classification 3MT, Driving Wheel 5ft 2in, Cylinders inside.

Collett '2251 Class' 0-6-0 3205 is an early example of preserved and restored steam power, pictured preparing to leave Bridgnorth Station on the Severn Valley Railway in 1970.

Number	Name	Class	Type	Ex Work	Builder	Ex BR	Location	Status 2009
3205		2251	2-6-0	1910	Sdn	1965	SDR (36)	Rebuild

City '3440 Class' designed by Churchward. This class of double frame locomotives originally consisted of 30 engines of which 10 were rebuilds from the 'Atbara Class'. City of Truro had the distinction of being the 2000th steam locomotive to be built at Swindon Works; importantly it was the first steam locomotive to be credited with achieving a speed of over 100mph. On 9 May 1904 City Of Truro allegedly reached a speed of 102.3mph while descending Wellington Bank in Devon. The claim was hard to substantiate or indeed totally disclaim, and is to this day still a talking point among enthusiasts. In 1912 the locomotive was renumbered 3717, it was withdrawn from GWR service in 1931 and placed in York Museum (now NRM). 'City of Truro' qualifies for inclusion in this publication because although it was withdrawn before BR came into being it did not stay in retirement! In 1957 British Railways removed the locomotive from the museum and gave it a complete overhaul, at Swindon Works. After BR Western Region returned 'City of Truro' to running order the loco was allocated the number 3440. Thereafter the loco was used regularly on enthusiast specials and ordinary service trains until again gaining the status of preserved locomotive in 1961. The locomotive was not allocated a BR power classification. Driving Wheel 6ft 8½in, Cylinders inside.

Number	Name	Class	Type	Ex Work	Builder	Ex BR	Location	Status 2009
3440	City of Truro	3440	4-4-0	1903	Sdn	1961	NRM (tours)	Operational

The iconic 3440 City of Truro pictured when the NRM-based record breaker visited the Churnet Valley Railway in 2005.

Star '4000 Class' a Churchward design, number series between 4003 and 4062. This type was the forerunner of all the four-cylinder express locomotives built by the GWR. Swindon Works built 72 of these engines between 1906 and 1923. Withdrawal from service started in 1932 with BR inheriting 47 examples. Power Classification 5P, Driving Wheel 6ft 8½in, Cylinders four.

Number	Name	Class	Type	Ex Work	Builder	Ex BR	Location	Status 2009
4003	Lode Star	4000	4-6-0	1907	Sdn	1951	NRM	Static display

Castle Class 4-6-0 5080 Defiant in full cry heading for Dee Bridge during a visit to the Llangollen Railway.

7027 Thornbury Castle was in 2008 still a long term restoration project. The Collett 4-6-0 is seen in BR service on the Didcot avoiding line with a Worcester/Hereford/Oxford-Paddington service. *David Anderson.*

4079 Pendennis Castle is pictured with a Stephenson Locomotive Society Swindon-Oxford-Birmingham special train on Didcot West Curve in April 1964. *David Anderson.*

Tyseley-based '4073 Class' 7029 Clun Castle on main line duty in 1978 is pictured at Chester with a Pullman coach.

Number	Name	Class	Type	Ex Works	Builder	Ex BR	Location	Status 2009
4073	Caerphilly Castle	4073	4-6-0	1924	Sdn	1960	Steam Musm Sdn	Static display
4079	Pendennis Castle	4073	4-6-0	1924	Sdn	1964	Didcot (19)	Rebuild
5029	Nunney Castle	4073	4-6-0	1934	Sdn	1963	Tyseley Loco Works	Operational
5043	Earl of Mount Edgcumbe*	4073	4-6-0	1936	Sdn	1963	Tyseley Loco Works	Operational
5051	Earl Bathurst *	4073	4-6-0	1936	Sdn	1963	Didcot (19)	Static display
5080	Defiant*	4073	4-6-0	1939	Sdn	1963	BRC (16)	Static display
7027	Thornbury Castle	4073	4-6-0	1949	Sdn	1963	L&NWR Heritage Crewe	Long Term
7029	Clun Castle	4073	4-6-0	1950	Sdn	1965	Tyseley Loco Works	Rebuild

*5043 named Barbury Castle March 1936, name changed September 1937. 5051 named Drysllwyn Castle May 1936, name changed August 1937. 5080 named Ogmore Castle May 1939, named changed January 1941.

Castle '4073 Class' was a Collett design, main number series 4073-4099, 5000-5099, 7000-7037. The highly successful 4-6-0 four-cylinder express passenger engines were built at Swindon Works between 1923 and 1947 under the GWR, and between 1948 and 1951 by British Railways. In total 171 of the class were built and they included six locomotives which were rebuilt from Churchwards Star Class, numbers 111, 4000, 4009, 4006, 4032, 4037. The 'Castles' were put in charge of the GWR's crack express services of the time, and perhaps the Cheltenham Flyer is one of the best known examples. That service between London Paddington and Cheltenham required the locomotives to average 62.2mph for the journey, allowing just 70 minutes to cover the 77.3 miles between Swindon and Paddington. There are many recorded instances of Castle Class locomotives when in the hands of a skilled crew attaining, and even topping, 100mph in regular service while hauling heavy trains. Power Classification 7P, Driving Wheel 6ft 8½in, Cylinders four.

'4200 Class' a Churchward design of powerful freight tank locomotives, number series 4200-4299, 5200-5204. The class of 2-8-0Ts were primarily built to work heavy 'short haul' coal and mineral trains in South Wales. They were the only 2-8-0 tank locomotives to work in the UK. They incorporated standard GWR component parts as used in the '2800 Class' of tender locomotives. Engines in the number series 4200-4299 and 5200-5204 had a Power Classification of 7F, Driving Wheel 4ft 7½in, Cylinders outside.

Above: **Beautifully restored '4200 Class' 4277' prepares to start a winter Saturday Carrog service from Glyndyfrdwy on the Llangollen Railway.**

Number	Name	Class	Type	Ex Works	Builder	Ex BR	Location	Status 2009
4247		4200	2-8-0T	1916	Sdn	1964	B&W (25)	Operational
4248		4200	2-8-0T	1916	Sdn	1963	Steam Musm Sdn	Static display
4253		4200	2-8-0T	1916	Sdn	1963	Pon&B (81)	Scrap cond
4270		4200	2-8-0T	1917	Sdn	1962	G&WR (48)	Long term
4277		4200	2-8-0T	1920	Sdn	1964	Pa/Dart (33)	Repair

Churchward '4200 Class' 2-8-0T 4253 was withdrawn by BR in 1963, once the 'Pride of the Valleys' the 1916-built 7F tank loco was still awaiting restoration when pictured in 2008.

Above: On preserved railways livery changes are not unusual; this 7325 is seen in BR unlined black, also at the SVR.

'4300 Class' a Churchward design, number series 4303-4386, 5300-5399, 6300-6399, 7300-7341. This Class built between 1911 and 1922 were the first 'modern' 2-6-0 (Moguls) built in the UK. The wheels and motions of locomotive of this class, withdrawn between 1936 and 1939, were used in the construction of the 'Grange' and 'Manor' class locomotives. Power Classification 4MT, Driving Wheel 5ft 8in, Cylinders outside.

Left: '4300 Class' 2-6-0 7325 pictured at Hampton Loade on the Severn Valley Railway this time in GWR green.

In addition to livery changes temporary identity changes also take place from time to time. This is 7325 masquerading as '9000 Class' 9303 at the SVR in 1992.

Number	Name	Class	Type	Ex Works	Builder	Ex BR	Location	Status 2009
5322		4300	2-6-0	1917	Sdn	1964	Didcot (19)	Operational
7325*		4300*	2-6-0	1932	Sdn	1964	SVR (59)	Static display

Has run in preservation as 9303 of the '9000 Class', a modified loco with ballast weights and side cab windows.

'4500 Class' a Churchward design, number series 4500-4574. This was one of three GWR classes known as 'Small Prairie Tanks'. They were a very popular class and used extensively on branch line work. The first 20 of the 75-strong class were among the last locomotives to be built at Wolverhampton, between 1906 and 1908. Power Classification as built 4MT, reclassified in 1953 as 3MT. Driving Wheel 4ft 7½in, Cylinders outside.

Churchward '4500 Class' 2-6-2T 4566 drifts into Bewdley Station on the SVR, February 1976.

Number	Name	Class	Type	Ex Works	Builder	Ex BR	Location	Status 2009
4555		4500	2-6-2T	1924	Sdn	1963	Pa/Dart (33)	Stored o/u
4561		4500	2-6-2T	1924	Sdn	1962	WSR (39)	Stored o/u
4566		4500	2-6-2T	1924	Sdn	1962	SVR (59)	Operational

'4575 Class' a Collett development of the 4500 Churchward design, number series 4574-4599, 5500-5574. These locomotives were also referred to as Small Prairie Tanks. BR inherited 100 of this class. Power Classification, as built 4MT, reclassified in 1953 as 3MT. Driving Wheel 4ft 7½in, Cylinders outside.

Left: '4575 Class' 2-6-2T in preservation, 5553 runs around its train at Minehead on the West Somerset Railway.

Number	Name	Class	Type	Ex Works	Builder	Ex BR	Location	Status 2009
4588		4575	2-6-2T	1927	Sdn	1962	Pa/Dart (33)	Stored o/u
5521		4575	2-6-2T	1927	Sdn	1962	Poland UK base(45)	Operational
5526		4575	2-6-2T	1928	Sdn	1962	SDR (36)	Operational
5532		4575	2-6-2T	1928	Sdn	1962	LR (80)	Restoration
5538		4575	2-6-2T	1928	Sdn	1961	Barry (72)	Restoration
5539		4575	2-6-2T	1928	Sdn	1962	LR (80)	Restoration
5541		4575	2-6-2T	1928	Sdn	1962	DeanF (45)	Repair
5542		4575	2-6-2T	1928	Sdn	1961	WSR (39)tours	Operational
5552		4575	2-6-2T	1928	Sdn	1960	B&W (25)	Operational
5553		4575	2-6-2T	1928	Sdn	1961	WSR (39)	Operational
5572		4575	2-6-2T	1929	Sdn	1962	Didcot (19)	Static display

'4575 Class' 2-6-2T in BR service, 5541 prepares to leave Barmouth on the ex Cambrian Railway in 1953.

Hall '4900 Class' a Collett-designed mixed traffic locomotive, number series 4900-4999, 5900-5999, 6900-6958. In 1924 Saint Class locomotive 2925 (built in 1903) was rebuilt with 6ft diameter driving wheels and other modifications, and as such it became the forerunner of the class of highly successful GWR '4900' locomotives which at their zenith totalled 258 engines; all of the class were named. During the 1946 coal crisis 11 of the class were modified to oil burning and renumbered in the 3900 series, they were reconverted – back to coal burning and re-given their old numbers between 1947-49. Power Classification 5MT, Driving Wheel 6ft 0in, Cylinders outside.

Left: **Modified Hall 4-6-0 6989 Wightwick Hall in BR service. Pictured at Oxford with a Worcester/Hereford-Paddington service. Note the fireman tending to the coal.** *David Anderson.*

Number	Name	Class	Type	Ex Works	Builder	Ex BR	Location	Status 2009
4920	Dumbleton Hall	4900	4-6-0	1929	Sdn	1962	SDR (36)	Long term
4930	Hagley Hall	4900	4-6-0	1929	Sdn	1962	SVR (59)	Static display
4936	Kinlet Hall	4900	4-6-0	1929	Sdn	1964	Tyseley Loco Works	Operational
4942	Maindy Hall**	4900	4-6-0	1929	Sdn	1963	N/A	N/A
4953	Pitchford Hall	4900	4-6-0	1929	Sdn	1963	Tyseley Loco Works	Operational
4965	Rood Ashton Hall	4900	4-6-0	1929	Sdn	1962	Tyseley Loco Works	Rebuild
4979	Wootton Hall	4900	4-6-0	1930	Sdn	1963	Private site Appleby	Scrap Cond
5900	Hinderton Hall	4900	4-6-0	1931	Sdn	1963	Didcot (19)	Stored o/u
5952	Cogan Hall	4900	4-6-0	1935	Sdn	1964	CRSoc(74)	Long term
5967	Bickmarsh Hall	4900	4-6-0	1937	Sdn	1964	Nrt&Lmp(53)	Long term
5972	Olton Hall*	4900	4-6-0	1937	Sdn	1963	West CoastRailway Co	Operational

*AKA Hogwarts Castle, as used in the Harry Potter films.   **Donor locomotive for GWR 1014 and GWR 6880.

Modified Hall '6959 Class' a Hawksworth development from the Collett '4900' class locomotives, built between 1944 and 1950 with the number series 6959-6999, 7900-7929. These locomotives had a redesigned boiler with a three row superheater and thus a greater superheating surface area. Power Classification 5MT, Driving Wheel 6ft 0in, Cylinders outside.

Number	Name	Class	Type	Ex Works	Builder	Ex BR	Location	Status 2009
6960	Raveningham Hall	6959	4-6-0	1944	Sdn	1964	G&WR (48)	Rebuild
6984	Owsden Hall	6959	4-6-0	1948	Sdn	1965	G&WR (48)	Restoration
6989	Wightwick Hall	6959	4-6-0	1948	Sdn	1964	BRS (16)	Restoration
6990	Witherslack Hall	6959	4-6-0	1948	Sdn	1965	GCR (49)	Rebuild
6998	Burton Agnes Hall	6959	4-6-0	1949	Sdn	1965	Didcot (19)	Static display
7903	Foremarke Hall	6959	4-6-0	1949	Sdn	1964	G&WR (48)	Operational
7927	Willington Hall*	6959	4-6-0	1950	Sdn	1965	N/A	N/A

*Donor loco providing parts for new build locomotives 6880 Betton Grange and 1014 County of Glamorgan.

British Steam

'4900 Class' 4-6-0 4930 Hagley Hall double heads into Chester with ex LMS Black Five 5000. The date 22 September 1979 as the pair prepare to work the Chester-Hereford return leg of the SVR Association's 'The Inter City' special train.

Left: Ex GWR 'Hall' 4-6-0 5967 Bickmarsh Hall in BR service. The loco is pictured a Newton Abbot in June 1959.

Below: Modified Hall 4-6-0 5990 Witherslack Hall, pictured in BR service at Didcot with a 'down' parcels. *David Anderson.*

Hall '4900 Class' 4-6-0
4930 Hagley Hall is
pictured on the Severn
Valley Railway in 1986.

Castle '7073 Class' 4-6-0 7029
Clun Castle is pictured on the
Severn Valley Railway in 1985.

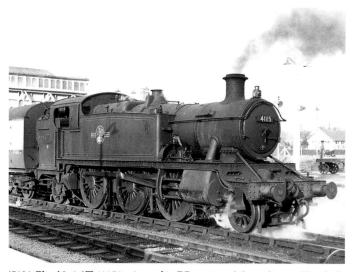

'5101 Class' 2-6-2T 4115 is pictured in BR service while working as Hereford Station pilot in January 1959. *David Anderson.*

'5101 Class' 2-6-2T 4141 shimmers in the summer sunshine while waiting to depart Llangollen with a service for Carrog.

Number	Name	Class	Type	Ex Works	Builder	Ex BR	Location	Status 2009
4110		5101	2-6-2T	1935	Sdn	1965	Tyseley Loco Works	Long term
4115		5101	2-6-2T	1936	Sdn	1965	Barry (72)	Scrap cond
4121		5101	2-6-2T	1937	Sdn	1965	Tyseley Loco Works	Scrap cond
4141		5101	2-6-2T	1946	Sdn	1963	GCR (49)	Operational
4144		5101	2-6-2T	1946	Sdn	1965	Didcot (19)	Static display
4150		5101	2-6-2T	1947	Sdn	1965	SVR (59)	Rebuild
4160		5101	2-6-2T	1948	Sdn	1965	WSR (39)	Operational
5164		5101	2-6-2T	1930	Sdn	1963	SVR (59)	Operational
5193*		5101	2-6-2T	1934	Sdn	1962	N/A	N/A
5199		5101	2-6-2T	1934	Sdn	1963	LR (80)	Operational

*Donor locomotive for new build loco number 9351 at the WSR.

Left: '5205 Class' 2-8-0T 5224 at Kingsley & Froghall on the Churnet Valley Railway.

'5101 Class' a Churchward design modified and rebuilt by Collett, known as Large Prairie Tanks. They were built between 1903-1906 and 1929-1949, number series 4100-4179 and 5101-5199. The highest total number of these engines operated by BR was 159 in 1950, 29 examples lasted until the end of steam on the GWR. Power Classification 4MT, Driving Wheel 5ft 8in, Cylinders outside.

'5205 Class' a Collett design built between 1923 and 1940 these locomotives were a more powerful development from the GWR '4200' Class, number series 5205-5264. Power Classification 8F, Driving Wheel 4ft 7½in, Cylinders outside.

Number	Name	Class	Type	Ex Works	Builder	Ex BR	Location	Status 2009
5224		5205	2-8-0T	1924	Sdn	1963	NYMR (99)	Operational
5227		5205	2-8-0T	1924	Sdn	1963	Barry (72)	Scrap cond
5239		5205	2-8-0T	1924	Sdn	1963	Pa/Dart (33)	Operational

'5600 Class' 0-6-2T 5637 in preservation, pictured with a demonstration freight train on the Llangollen Railway.

5600 Class' a Collett-designed tank locomotive, specifically for working coal trains in the Welsh Valleys, built between 1924 and 1928 at GWR Swindon and Armstrong Whitworth, GWR number series 5600-5699, 6600-6699. BR inherited 200 of class. Power Classification 5MT, Driving Wheel 4ft 7½in, Cylinders inside.

Number	Name	Class	Type	Ex Works	Builder	Ex BR	Location	Status 2009
5619		5600	0-6-2T	1925	Sdn	1964	G&WR (48)	Operational
5637		5600	0-6-2T	1925	Sdn	1964	ESR (28)	Restoration
5643		5600	0-6-2T	1925	Sdn	1963	L&H (112) Tours	Operational
5668		5600	0-6-2T	1926	Sdn	1964	Pon&B (81)	Scrap cond
6619		5600	0-6-2T	1928	Sdn	1963	NYM (99)	Operational
6634		5600	0-6-2T	1928	Sdn	1964	LNWR Crewe	Long term
6686		5600	0-6-2T	1928	AW	1964	Barry (72)	Scrap cond
6695		5600	0-6-2T	1928	AW	1964	SwanR(37)	Operational
6697		5600	0-6-2T	1928	AW	1966	Didcot (19)	Static display

'5600 Class' 0-6-2T 6634 in BR service, pictured rumbling through the centre road at Cardiff Central in 1959.

PANNIER TANKS UNMISTAKABLY GREAT WESTERN

'5700 Class' 0-6-0PT 9600, Tyseley based. *Brian Wilson.*

'5700 Class' a Collett-designed Pannier Tank class built between 1929 and 1939 with the number series 3600-3777, 4600-4699, 5700-5799, 7700-7799, 8700-8799, 9600-9682, 9711-9799. Although they did work in other regions, and for other railway companies, the pannier tank type is almost always identified as being associated with the Great Western Railway. Developed from earlier types the '5700 Class' was introduced primarily for shunting and light goods work but were also extensively used on branch passenger services.

In total some 863 were built (including the later 6700 and 9700 versions) by the GWR and seven outside contractors. BR inherited 762 of the class in 1948 thereafter taking into stock a further 10 locomotives.

Between 1956 and 1963 London Transport bought a batch from BR and numbered them in their own series as L89 to L99. Number L91 was allocated by LT to two different engines 5752 (1957-60) and 5757 (1960-1967). Several LT pannier tanks operated after the end of steam on BR with L92 (5786) remaining in service until September 1969, L99 (7715) until December 1969, L89 (5775) until January 1970, and L90 (7760), L94 (7752) and L95 (5764) until June 1971, when steam on the LT ended. Preserved examples have operated in LT livery. Power Classification 4F, Driving Wheel 4ft 7½in, Cylinders inside.

Locomotive number 5775, based at the Keighley and Worth Valley Railway, featured in the film The Railway Children; it was painted brown and lettered as a loco of the fictitious Great Northern and Southern Railway.

'5700 Class' 0-6-0PT L94 (BR 7752) seen in London Transport livery.

'5700 Class' 0-6-0PT 7754, Llangollen Railway based.

'5700 Class' 0-6-0PT 5775, based at the Keighley & Worth Valley Railway.

'5700 Class' 0-6-0PT 9682, Chinnor & Princes Risborough based.

Number	Name	Class	Type	Ex Works	Builder	Ex BR	Location	Status 2009
3612*		5700	0-6-0PT	1939	Sdn	1964	N/A	N/A
3650		5700	0-6-0PT	1939	Sdn	1963	Didcot (19)	Operational
3738		5700	0-6-0PT	1937	Sdn	1965	Didcot (19)	Operational
4612		5700	0-6-0PT	1942	Sdn	1965	B&W (25)	Operational
5764 L95		5700	0-6-0PT	1929	Sdn	1960 LT 1971	SVR (59)	Operational
5775 L89		5700	0-6-0PT	1929	Sdn	1963 LT 1970	K&WVR (95)	Stored o/u
5786 L92		5700	0-6-0PT	1930	Sdn	1958 LT 1969	SDR (36)	Operational
7714		5700	0-6-0PT	1930	KS	1959	SVR (59)	Operational
7715 L99		5700	0-6-0PT	1930	KS	1963 LT 1969	BRC (16)	Under repair
7752 L94		5700	0-6-0PT	1930	NBL	1959 LT 1971	Tyseley Loco Works	Stored o/u
7754		5700	0-6-0PT	1930	NBL	1959	LR (80)	Rebuild
7760 L90		5700	0-6-0PT	1930	NBL	1962 LT 1971	Tyseley Loco Works	Stored o/u
9600		5700	0-6-0PT	1945	Sdn	1965	Tyseley Loco Works	Operational
9629		5700	0-6-0PT	1945	Sdn	1964	Pon&B (81)	Long term
9642		5700	0-6-0PT	1945	Sdn	1964	G&WR (48)	Rebuild
9681		5700	0-6-0PT	1949	Sdn	1965	DeanF (45)	Operational
9682		5700	0-6-0PT	1949	Sdn	1965	ChinPR (17)	Operational

*Donor locomotive for spares, including second rebuild of 7754.

'5700 Class' 0-6-0PT 7714 double heads with 5764, both Severn Valley Railway based.

'5700 Class' 0-6-0PT 5764, Severn Valley Railway based.

Preserved

Above: 'Leader of the Class' Collett 'King' 4-6-0 6000 King George V heads the 'Western Jubilee' working on 8 June 1977 between Craven Arms and Shrewsbury.

Right: The bell presented to 6000 KGV by the Baltimore and Ohio Railroad of the USA.

Below: Climbing 'King'. 6000 King George V storms Gresford Bank during a main line special run from Chester to Hereford.

King '6000 Class' a Collett design considered to be the ultimate development of GWR four-cylinder locomotives. Built at Swindon between 1927 and 1930 the class totalled 30 locomotives, in the number series 6000-6029. The directors of the GWR wanted to regain the 'most powerful express passenger steam locomotive in Britain' title, which had been taken from Collett's Castle Class in 1926 by the Southern Railway Lord Nelson Class. Collett's clever design easily won

back that title. The first of the class, 6000 King George V, appeared in 1927 and was sent on a tour of North America, for the Centenary celebrations of the Baltimore and Ohio Railroad (B&O), where its sleek appearance and smooth performance impressed all concerned. The locomotive was presented with a brass bell to mark the occasion, which to this day it carries on the buffer beam. An original naming scheme planned for the '6000 Class' was to name them after cathedrals, but when the American trip was planned, an unmistakably British icon was needed, and so they became 'Kings'. Often dubbed 'Super-Castles' by those involved with their construction the class perhaps enjoyed its best performances in British Railways ownership, particularly with express services on the fearsome South Devon banks at Dainton, Rattery and Hemerdon. They were engines to be reckoned with; powering the Western Region's crack expresses like the Cornish Riviera Limited up until the end of regular steam-hauled express services on the WR. Power Classification as built 7P, reclassified in 1951 to 8P. Driving Wheel 6ft 6in, Cylinders four.

On 10 June 2008, 6024 hauled the Royal Train, with the Prince of Wales and Duchess of Cornwall on board, from Kidderminster Town to Bridgnorth on the Severn Valley Railway.

Above: **Collett 'King' 4-6-0 on Royal Train duty. On 10 June 2008, 6024 hauled the Royal Train, with the Prince of Wales and Duchess of Cornwall on the Severn Valley Railway. The three-headlamp code was used, as opposed to the four-headlamp Royal Code which is reserved for the reigning monarch.** *Malcolm Whittaker.*

Left: **'King' under the wires. 6024 King Edward I is pictured on the West Coast Main Line at Moore in March 1998 with 'The Cumbrian Mountain Express'.**

Number	Name	Class	Type	Ex Works	Builder	Ex BR	Location	Status 2009
6000	King George V	6000	4-6-0	1927	Sdn	1962	NRM	Static display
6023	King Edward II	6000	4-6-0	1930	Sdn	1962	Didcot (19)	Restoration
6024	King Edward I	6000	4-6-0	1930	Sdn	1962	Tyseley Loco Works	Operational

'6100 Class' a Collett design built between 1931 and 1935 in the number series 6100-6169. British Railways inherited all 70 of this class which was a variation of the '5100 Class' intended for London suburban services. Power Classification as built 4MT reclassified in 1953 to 5MT. Driving Wheel 5ft 8in, Cylinders outside.

Right: **Collett '6100 Class' 2-6-2T is seen in BR service 'on shed' at Southall in 1965, the loco is in the company of sister loco 6159 and Stanier 8F 48120 (both unpreserved).**

Number	Name	Class	Type	Ex Work	Builder	Ex BR	Location	Status 2009
6106		6100	2-6-2T	1931	Sdn	1965	Didcot (19)	Static Display

'6400 Class' a Collett design of pannier tank which was a variation of the '5400 Class' with smaller wheels. Built between 1932 and 1937 they carried the number series 6400-6439. Power Classification 2P, Driving Wheel 4ft 7½in, Cylinders inside.

Number	Name	Class	Type	Ex Works	Builder	Ex BR	Location	Status 2009
6412		6400	0-6-0PT	1934	Sdn	1964	WSR (39)	Rebuild
6430		6400	0-6-0PT	1937	Sdn	1964	LR (80)	Operational
6435		6400	0-6-0PT	1937	Sdn	1964	B&W (25)	Operational

'7200 Class' Collett rebuilds from '5205' and '4200' classes, with the number series 7200-7253. Power Classification 8F, Driving Wheel 4ft 7½in, Cylinders outside.

Number	Name	Class	Type	Ex Works	Builder	Ex BR	Location	Status 2009
7200		7200	2-8-2T	1930	Sdn	1963	BRC (16)	Restoration
7202		7200	2-8-2T	1930	Sdn	1964	Didcot (19)	Restoration
7229		7200	2-8-2T	1926	Sdn	1964	ELR (109)	Restoration

Manor '7800 Class' a Collett design which was a lighter version of the '6800 Class' Grange locomotives built between 1938-1939 and in 1950; 30 locomotives in the number series 7800-7829, the last 10 built by BR entered service in 1950. They were built for lines with restricted route availability ie the main lines of the old Midland & South Western Junction and the Cambrian Railways. All but one of the class worked up to the end of 1963 (7809 Childrey Manor) and 19 examples served BR beyond the end of 1964. Power Classification 5MT, Driving Wheel 5ft 8in, Cylinders outside.

Number	Name	Class	Type	Ex Works	Builder	Ex BR	Location	Status 2009
7802	Bradley Manor	7800	4-6-0	1938	Sdn	1965	SVR (59)	Operational
7808	Cookham Manor	7800	4-6-0	1938	Sdn	1965	Didcot (19)	Static Display
7812	Erlestoke Manor	7800	4-6-0	1939	Sdn	1965	SVR (59)	Operational
7819	Hinton Manor	7800	4-6-0	1939	Sdn	1965	Swindon Designer Outlet	Static display
7820	Dinmore Manor	7800	4-6-0	1950	Sdn	1965	WSR (39)	Rebuild
7821	Ditcheat Manor	7800	4-6-0	1950	Sdn	1965	WSR (39)	Rebuild
7822	Foxcote Manor	7800	4-6-0	1950	Sdn	1965	LR (80)	Operational
7827	Lydham Manor	7800	4-6-0	1950	Sdn	1965	Pa/Dart (33)	Operational
7828	Odney Manor	7800	4-6-0	1950	Sdn	1965	WSR (39)	Rebuild

'9000 Class' Collett introductions between 1936 and 1939, known as the GWR 'Dukedog' or 'Earl' type of locomotives. They incorporated parts recycled from earlier Dean-built engines. The class was generally known as 'Dukedogs' and were to be seen at work under BR on the Cambrian lines in Wales and prior to that on the Didcot/Newbury-Southampton line. BR inherited 26 of the class and 9017 was one of the last five to serve, being withdrawn in October 1960. Power Classification 2P/2MT, Driving Wheel 5ft 8in, Cylinders inside.

Number	Name	Class	Type	Ex Work	Builder	Ex BR	Location	Status 2009
9017	Earl Of Berkeley*	9000	4-4-0	1906	Sdn	1960	Bbell (2)	Operational

*Name allocated in preservation

'9400 Class' a Hawksworth design introduced between 1947 and 1956 and built by BR Swindon and various subcontractors. Allocated the number series 3400-3409, 8400-8499, 9400-9499, these were the last of a long line of GWR pannier tanks. The last example (3409) built by the Yorkshire Engine Co Ltd did not enter service until December 1956 (withdrawn December 1964) thus serving BR for only eight years. Power Classification 4F, Driving Wheel 4ft 7 1/2in, Cylinders inside.

Hawksworth '9400 Class' 9466 is pictured during a 1997 SVR Gala weekend.

Number	Name	Class	Type	Ex Works	Builder	Ex BR	Location	Status 2009
9400		9400	0-6-0PT	1947	Sdn	1959	NRMSteam Swindon	Static display
9466		9400	0-6-0PT	1952	RSH	1964	Tyseley Loco Works	Operational

'S&M 1' designed by Dodman, Lynn for the Shropshire & Montgomery Railway in 1893 as a 2-2-2WT and rebuilt as 0-4-2WT in 1911. The S&M was taken over by the War Department during WWII as it served several important armaments factories. In 1950 the loco was taken into BR Western Region stock and withdrawn without being renumbered. The loco was placed on display at the Longmoor home of the Transportation Corps in 1950 and for sometime stood on the edge of the parade ground. Driving Wheel 2ft 0in, Cylinders inside.

Number	Name	Class	Type	Ex Work	Builder	Ex BR	Location	Status 2009
1	Gazelle	S&M1	0-4-2WT	1911	S&M	1950	K&ESR (9)	Static display

NEW BUILDS
WORK IN PROGRESS

'1000 Class' County. No example from this Hawkesworth-designed class of 30 locomotives was preserved. They were the GWR's final development of the two cylinder 4-6-0 express locomotive type and were direct descendants of the '2900 Class' Star locomotives. The 'Counties' were in effect a larger version of the Modified Hall '6959' Class. Distinctive in appearance the class had one large 'splasher' covering all the wheels and a straight instead of curved nameplate. From 1955 onwards they were all rebuilt with double chimneys. They were named after counties served by the GWR. Power Classification 6MT, Driving Wheel 6ft 3in, Cylinders outside.

The new, locomotive to be named 'County of Glamorgan' and given that loco's BR number, is being built at the Didcot Railway Centre (19), home of the Great Western Society. The replica locomotive will have the frames from Hall Class No 7927 Willington Hall and the boiler from LMS Stanier 8F No 48518. It will also have a number of original parts from scrapped County locomotives, including the chimney from No 1006 County of Cornwall.

'6800 Class' Grange. The Collett-designed GWR 'Grange' class built between 1936 and 1939 consisted of 80 locomotives which were described as versions of the 'Hall' class with smaller wheels, number series 6800-6879. No examples of the class were preserved. They were built to replace life-expired '4300' class 2-6-0s and BR took into stock all 80 Granges, with 45 locos staying in service until 1965. The intention was to replace all of the '4300' class with 'Granges' and 'Manors' (which were built at the same time) but the second world war intervened and that plan was never completed. 'Grange' and 'Manor' locomotives were lower in height than the 'Hall' class accordingly they had a raised section of running plate over the cylinders. Power Classification 5MT, Driving Wheel 5ft 8in, Cylinders outside.

The '6880 Society' was formed in 1998 with the sole intention of recreating a Great Western Grange class locomotive. The society has chosen Llangollen Railway Engineering (80) as their partners in this venture and they are located at that railway. The boiler from donor locomotive 7927 Willington Hall is to be used in the replication of the 6880 'Betton Grange'.

No Hawksworth '1000' County Class locomotives survived into preservation but the Great Western Society are currently (2008) building one. That finished locomotive will be 1014 County of Glamorgan. Pictured in BR service is 1022 County of Northampton which is seen passing Chester No 6 signalbox (no longer in situ) in August 1958. 1022 was built at Swindon, entering service in December 1946 and being withdrawn in October 1962, the loco was not cut up until January 1964.

Pictured at Tyseley MPD in June 1960 is 6853 Morehampton Grange.

'2900 Class' Saint. The Churchward-designed GWR Saint class, built between 1902 and 1913 was the forerunner of a long line of 4-6-0 express locomotives with the number series 2900, 2902-2989, no examples were preserved. When built, the prototype for the class, No 2900 'William Dean', was the first GWR engine to carry outside cylinders. In total 77 'Saint' class locomotives were built. In 1924 loco No 2925 'Saint Martin' was rebuilt with modifications to become 4900 the prototype of the 'Hall Class'. Withdrawal of the Saints started in 1931, 39 were recorded as BR WR stock at the end of 1948. The last to be withdrawn was No 2920 'Saint David' in October 1953, it was cut up a month later. Power Classification 4P, Driving Wheel 6ft 8½in, Cylinders outside.

The Great Western Society based at Didcot Railway Centre (19) is reversing history and recreating a Saint Class locomotive by rebuilding a Hall Class locomotive No 4942 'Maindy Hall' to replicate a Saint 4-6-0, as built in 1913.

Number	Name	Class	Type	Start Date	Builder	Donor loco	Location	Status 2009
1014	Country of Glamorgan	1000 County	4-6-0	2004	GW Society	GWR 7927 LMS 48518	Didcot (19)	Work in progress
2999	Lady of Legend	2900 Saint	4-6-0	2004	GW Society	GWR 4942	Didcot (19)	Work in progress
6880	Betton Grange	6800 Grange	4-6-0	1998	6880 Society	GWR 7927	LR (80)	Work in progress

Celebrating the past! Castle '4073 Class' 4-6-0 5051 Earl Bathurst is pictured on Welsh Marches Pullman duty during May 1983 carrying the name Drysllwyn Castle which 'she' carried briefly in GWR ownership (May 1936 to August 1937) being renamed thereafter.

BUILT IN MINEHEAD –
WEST SOMERSET RAILWAY No. 9351

New Build – in service. Locomotive No 9351 of the West Somerset Railway. This loco is the result of a radical rebuild of a former ex-GWR Large Prairie 2-6-2T (No 5193) and is designed around the proposed GWR Small Mogul type (2-6-0) The new tender type loco carries the number 9351 – which follows GWR practice for the first of a new class. The conversion has created considerable debate amongst the heritage railway community. Power Classification 4 MT, as 5193, Driving Wheel 5ft 8in, Cylinders outside.

Number	Class	Type	Start Date	Builder	Donor loco	Location	Status 2009
9351	WSR 9351	2-6-0	2000	WSR GWR	5193	WSR (39)	Operational

EX BR LMS
LOCOMOTIVES

At their formation in January 1948 British Railways took into stock 7821 ex LMS steam locomotives, many from the original 11 companies which were amalgamated in 1923 railway groupings to form the LMS. The London Midland & Scottish Region of BR utilised steam locomotive numbers in the series 40001 to 59999.

By the end of 1960 the London Midland Region total of ex LMS operational steam locomotives was 5155 and in 1963 the total had reduced to 3060. By the end of 1966 the region's total of standard gauge steam locomotives in regular service was 1024.

A total of 307 ex LMS locomotives were available to BR as the last year of steam operation dawned. That number was made up of only three types, which were all tender locomotives; there were 151 'Black Five' 4-6-0s, 150 'Stanier 8F' 2-8-0s and six 'Ivatt Mogul' 2-6-0s.

Preserved ex BR LMS locomotives total 85 examples; it is the second biggest total of rescued steam engines from any of the pre nationalisation railway companies. In addition there is currently one LMS design 'new build' project under way.

LMS Ivatt 2-6-0 No 46521 leads sister engine 46443 as they double head towards Hampton Loade on the SVR.

MR Deeley 4-4-0 Compound a Midland Railway design which many observers considered to be the most successful 'Compound' type to run in the UK. BR inherited 45 of the type but all were withdrawn by the end of 1951. The LMS built a further 195 variants of the type between 1924 and 1932. BR number series, Deeley locomotives 41000 to 41044 (7ft 0in driving wheels) and LMS/Fowler locomotives 41045 to 41199 (6ft 9in driving wheels). Power Classification 4P, Cylinders one inside high pressure, and two outside low pressure.

Right: **National Collection locomotive ex Midland Railway Compound No 1000 is pictured at Clifton Manchester in May 1980. The steam locomotive is headed by a Class 47 diesel because of a perceived fire risk.**

Number	Name	Class	Type	Ex Works	Builder	Ex BR	Location	Status 2009
41000		4P	4-4-0	1902	Derby	1959*	NRM/SVR(59)	Static display

*After being withdrawn this loco was fully restored by BR and painted in MR c1914 livery; it then worked main line specials before becoming museum based.

LMS Ivatt 2-6-2T a class of 130 compact tank locomotives built between 1946 and 1952, and intended for use on cross-country secondary passenger services and general branch line work. BR numbers 41200 to 41329. This type was the forerunner of the BR Standard '84000' series tank class. Locomotive No 41272 was the 7000th steam locomotive, built at Crewe Works. Numbers 41210-41229 and 41270-41289 were configured for 'push pull' train working (motor fitted). Power Classification 2MT, Driving Wheel 5ft 0in, cylinders outside.

Right: **LMS Ivatt 2-6-2T No 41241 is pictured about to take water at the Keighley & Worth Valley Railway in the early days of steam locomotive preservation.**

LMS Ivatt 2-6-2T No 41312 is seen double heading with 46521 in September 1999 at the Severn Valley Railway. 41312 is based at the Mid Hants Railway.

Number	Name	Class	Type	Ex Works	Builder	Ex BR	Location	Status 2009
41241		2MT	2-6-2T	1949	Crw	1966	K&WVR (95)	Operational
41298		2MT	2-6-2T	1951	Crw	1967	BRC (16)	Rebuild
41312		2MT	2-6-2T	1952	Crw	1967	Mid H (11)	Operational
41313		2MT	2-6-2T	1952	Crw	1965	IOW (8)	Scrap cond

MR Johnson 0-6-0T a Johnson design of which 340 examples were built by MR, LMS and the outside contractors Vulcan Foundry Ltd and Robert Stephenson & Co Ltd, between 1878 and 1902. BR inherited 95 of the class and placed them in the number series 41660 to 41895. Some engines were constructed with fully enclosed cabs while others (including the preserved example) carried only half cabs. One engine from the class was rebuilt as a diesel shunting loco in 1932; therefore LMS No 1831 was the forerunner of all the diesel shunters built by the LMS and BR. Power Classification 1F, Driving Wheel 4ft 7in, Cylinders inside.

Midland Railway Johnson 0-6-0T No 41708. This picture illustrates perfectly the 'half cab' design.

Number	Name	Class	Type	Ex Works	Builder	Ex BR	Location	Status 2009
41708		1F	0-6-0T	1880	Der	1966	BHill (41)	Operational

LTSR 4-4-2T a Whitelegg design for the London Tilbury & Southend Railway, introduced between 1909 and 1935. BR took into stock 51 examples and allocated them the numbers 41928 to 41978/41980; 16 locos carried names while in LTSR ownership. None survived into service beyond 1960. Power Classification 3P, Driving Wheel 6ft 6in, Cylinders outside.

Right: **Johnson 0-6-0T No 41847 is not what it seems! In fact the loco pictured at the Avon Valley Railway is 41708 masquerading as a sister loco which was not preserved, furthermore the 'half cab' is fitted with a removable cab back.**

Number	Name	Class	Type	Ex Works	Builder	Ex BR	Location	Status 2009
41966	Thundersley	3P	4-4-2T	1909	RS	1956*	Bressingham	Static display

*Restored by BR as No 80 Thundersley in March 1956, withdrawn May 1956.

LMS Fairburn 2-6-4T was a development from earlier Stanier classes of 2-6-4T two-cylinder tank locomotives introduced between 1945 and 1951, with the BR number series 42050 to 42299 and 42673 to 42699. They could be distinguished from the Stanier engines by a gap in the running plate ahead of the cylinders; they also had a slightly shorter wheelbase. Although an LMS design, the class was distributed all around the BR regions. Power Classification 4P (as built) reclassified to 4MT in 1948. Driving Wheel 5ft 9in, Cylinders outside.

Left: **LMS Fairburn 2-6-4T No 42073 in LMS livery as 2073 attracts a lot of attention when displayed at Carnforth in the early days of preservation. June 1969.**

Number	Name	Class	Type	Ex Works	Builder	Ex BR	Location	Status 2009
42073		4MT	2-6-4T	1950	Bton	1967	LS&H (112)	Operational
42085		4MT	2-6-4T	1951	Bton	1967	LS&H (112)	Operational

LMS Stanier 2-6-4T Locomotives of the 2-6-4T design were first introduced to the LMS by Fowler in 1927. In 1934 Stanier introduced a three-cylinder 2-6-4T for working the London Tilbury and Southend section of the LMS, with the BR number series 42500 to 42536. They were a development of Fowler's earlier two-cylinder design but with tapered boilers and sloping tops to the water tanks. The engines spent their entire working lives on the LTS until replaced in the early 1960s by electric multiple units. Power Classification 4P (as built) reclassified to 4MT in 1948. Driving Wheel 5ft 9in, Cylinders three.

Number	Name	Class	Type	Ex Works	Builder	Ex BR	Location	Status 2009
42500		4MT	2-6-4T	1934	Der	1962	NRM York	Static display

Hughes/Fowler 'Crab' 2-6-0 a highly successful mixed traffic 'Mogul' locomotive built between 1926 and 1932 for the LMS and allocated the BR number series 42700 to 42944. Crewe-built locomotive 42878 (LMS number 13178) was officially declared as being the 6000th engine built as Crewe but that is a claim disputed by some railway historians.

The Mogul type of wheel arrangement originated in the USA during the mid 1850s and the configuration was not commonly used in Britain during the early years of steam locomotive development. The Chief Mechanical Engineer of the LMSR from 1923 to 1925 was George Hughes and he designed the then ground-breaking LMS Mogul type. However Hughes retired before the 245 members of the class were completed, leaving his successor Henry Fowler to supervise their construction.

The design certainly looked different. With their two outside cylinders set at an inclined angle the front running board of the engines needed to be raised. Additionally the Hughes design utilised a parallel boiler, and that appeared to 'squat' between the frames. The combination of those features resulted in the engines being accorded the name 'Crabs'.

Power Classification 5F (as built) reclassified to 5MT/6P5F in 1948. Driving Wheel 5ft 6in, cylinders outside.

Hughes Fowler 'Crab' No 42765 is pictured hard at work departing Irwell Vale on the East Lancashire Railway.

Number	Name	Class	Type	Ex Works	Builder	Ex BR	Location	Status 2009
42700		5MT	2-6-0	1926	Hor	1966	NRM Locomotion	Static display
42765		5MT	2-6-0	1927	Crw	1966	ELR (109)	Rebuild
42859		5MT	2-6-0	1930	Crw	1966	Private site	Scrap cond

LMS Stanier 2-6-0 was a design for the LMS, built between 1933 and 1934 at Crewe Works. The 40 locomotives in the class carried the BR numbers 42945 to 42984. Following on from the highly successful 'Crab' moguls, the LMS in 1933 ordered a further class of 2-6-0s to complement their stock of mixed traffic locomotives. The company's Chief Mechanical Engineer, William Stanier, took inspiration for his design from an earlier class of GWR mogul.

The first member of the class (allocated LMS number 13245) emerged from Crewe Works on 21 October 1933. The new engine was married up to a six-wheel, Fowler-designed tender, as Stanier's own tender design had not at that time been completed. After 40 locos had been built the LMS postponed construction in order to make way for the imminent and intensive 'Black Five' 4-6-0 building programme. In the event production of the 'Stanier Mogul' was never resumed.

When they first entered traffic the Stanier moguls were sent in batches to each of the four LMS regions as they became available. Eventually most of the class became concentrated on the Western Division of the company, and were allocated to the depots at Crewe South, Mold Junction and Nuneaton. Although the locos were designed as freight engines, they also worked very successfully hauling passenger services. Power Classification 5F (as built) reclassified to 5MT/6P5F in 1948, Driving Wheel 5ft 6in, Cylinders outside.

Number	Name	Class	Type	Ex Works	Builder	Ex BR	Location	Status 2009
42968		5MT	2-6-0	1934	Crw	1966	SVR (59)	Operational

LMS Stanier 2-6-0 No 2968 (LMS number) is pictured at Bewdley on the Severn Valley Railway in 1992, coupled with a Fowler-designed tender.

LMS Stanier 2-6-0 No 2968, out on main line duty. The loco is pictured 'under the wires' at Crewe Station, on this occasion coupled to a Stanier-designed tender.

LMS Ivatt 'Mogul' No 43106 in BR service, pictured in ex works condition at Oxford MPD. *David Anderson*

LMS Ivatt 'Mogul' 2-6-0 No 43106 seen at Bridgnorth SVR in the early days of preservation (July 1970) note the GWR railcar.

LMS Ivatt 'Mogul' 2-6-0 was designed in 1947 for the LMS and 162 of the class were built between 1947 and 1952; they were allocated the LMS number series 43000 to 43161. In fact the LMS only built three of the class prior to the creation of BR, who then built the remainder of the type at Horwich, Doncaster and Darlington works. Engines 43000 to 43049 were originally fitted with double chimneys which in service proved to be unsatisfactory. After they were converted to single blast pipe, single chimney engines the steam production capability of their boilers was almost doubled. As the last year of steam operation on BR dawned six members of the class were still at work. The Riddles BR Standard '76000' series locomotives were based on this design. Power Classification 4F (as built) reclassified to 4MT in 1948, Driving Wheel 5ft 3in, Cylinders outside.

Number	Name	Class	Type	Ex Works	Builder	Ex BR	Location	Status 2009
43106		4MT	2-6-0	1951	Dar	1968	SVR (59)	Rebuild

MR Fowler 0-6-0 class built between 1911 and 1922. Totalling 192 locos the type was allocated the BR numbers 43835 to 44026. This class was Fowler's final development of the 0-6-0 type for the Midland Railway and the forerunner of a later 0-6-0 class built by the LMS. BR inherited all of the class and 21 examples survived to work into 1964, their last year of operation. Power Classification 4F, Driving Wheel 5ft 3in, Cylinders inside.

Left: **Midland Railway Fowler 0-6-0 class No 43924 is pictured at the Keighley & Worth Valley Railway. The yellow stripe on the cab side is to indicate that the loco could not work south of Crewe on the WCML and would have been applied to all steam locomotives working the region when the overhead electrification first became energised.**

Number	Name	Class	Type	Ex Works	Builder	Ex BR	Location	Status 2009
43924		4F	0-6-0	1920	Der	1965	K&WVR (95)	Rebuild

LMS & SDJR Fowler 0-6-0 was the class which after grouping in 1923 became the standard 0-6-0 freight locomotive for the LMS, it was a development of the '43835' Class Midland Railway type. Construction of the 580 locos in the class was carried out between 1924 and 1940 at the LMS locomotive works of Derby, Crewe, St Rollox and Horwich and by contractors North British Locomotive Co Ltd, Kerr Stewart & Co Ltd and Andrew Barclay Sons & Co Ltd. Earlier five of the type (44557-44561) were built by the Midland Railway for the Somerset & Dorset Joint Railway and carried that companies numbers 57 to 61, they came into LMS stock in 1930. By 1966 the number of the class employed by BR had dropped to 11 engines, and that was their last year of operation. Power Classification 4F, Driving Wheel 5ft 3in, Cylinders inside.

LMS & SDJR Fowler 0-6-0 with LMS number 4422 is pictured during an LMS themed gala at the Llangollen Railway. Themed events depicting past railway scenes are regularly held at preserved railways.

LMS & SDJR Fowler 0-6-0 No 44422 pictured with a rake of Windcutter Wagons (demonstration freight train) at the Great Central Railway. *David Gibson.*

Number	Name	Class	Type	Ex Works	Builder	Ex BR	Location	Status 2009
44027		4F	0-6-0	1924	Der	1964	NRM	Stored o/u
44123		4F	0-6-0	1925	Crw	1965	AVR (24)	Restoration
44422		4F	0-6-0	1927	Der	1965	ELR (109) Tours	Operational

LMS livery and number for National Collection 'Black Five' 4-6-0 No 5000, pictured double heading with SVR based Standard Tank 80079, on main line duty at Chester in May 1980.

East Lancashire Railway based Black Five No 45407 is pictured on the Conwy Valley Line ex Llandudno Junction en-route to Blaenau Ffestiniog with a 'Conway Climber' special. *Sue Langston*

North York Moors Railway based Black Five No 4767 is pictured with LMS livery and number. *Sue Langston.*

LMS Stanier 'Black Five' class designed by Stanier for the LMS was built between 1934 and 1951 by Armstrong Whitworth & Co (327), Vulcan Foundry (100), Derby (100), Horwich (105) and Crewe Works (210), 842 locos built in total. They were allocated the BR numbers 44658 to 45499. The first of the class to enter service was, in fact, the 21st in the LMS number sequence, No 5020 left the works of Vulcan Foundry, Newton-le-Willows, in August 1934. The record for the largest single order placed by a railway company concerned 227 engines of this class, and it was awarded to Tyneside engineers Sir WG Armstrong Whitworth & Co Ltd.

No less than 11 variants of the class were produced and withdrawal of the class started in 1961. Significantly, seven years later, on 4 August 1968, it was 'Black Five' No 45212 that had the dubious honour of hauling the last timetabled steam train for British Railways. The following week three 'Black Fives', Nos 44781, 44871 and 45110, were involved in the last rites that officially commemorated the end of the steam era on BR. Power Classification 5MT, Driving Wheel 6ft 0in, Cylinders outside.

Severn Valley based Black Five No 45110 pictured over the ash pit at Bewdley MPD.

Number	Name	Class	Type	Ex Works	Builder	Ex BR	Location	Status 2009
44767	George Stephenson*	5MT	4-6-0	1947	Crw	1967	NYMR (99)	Rebuild
44806	Kenneth Aldcroft*	5MT	4-6-0	1944	Der	1968	LR (80)	Operational
44871		5MT	4-6-0	1945	Crw	1968	ELR (109)	Restoration
44901		5MT	4-6-0	1945	Crw	1965	Barry (72)	Scrap cond
44932		5MT	4-6-0	1945	Hor	1968	MRC (50)	Rebuild
45000		5MT	4-6-0	1935	Crw	1967	NRM York	Static display
45025		5MT	4-6-0	1934	VF	1968	Strasp (108)	Stored o/u
45110	RAF Biggin Hill*	5MT	4-6-0	1935	VF	1968	SVR (59)	Operational
45163		5MT	4-6-0	1935	AW	1965	ColnVa (63)	Restoration
45212		5MT	4-6-0	1935	AW	1968	NYMR (99)	Operational
45231	The Sherwood Forester*	5MT	4-6-0	1936	AW	1968	ELR (109)	Operational
45293		5MT	4-6-0	1936	AW	1965	ColnVa (63)	Restoration
45305	Alderman A E Draper*	5MT	4-6-0	1937	AW	1968	GCR (49)	Rebuild
45337		5MT	4-6-0	1937	AW	1965	ELR (109)	Rebuild
45379		5MT	4-6-0	1937	AW	1965	MHants (11)	Operational
45407	The Lancashire Fusilier*	5MT	4-6-0	1937	AW	1968	ELR (109)	Operational
45428	Eric Treacy*	5MT	4-6-0	1937	AW	1967	NYMR (99)	Rebuild
45491		5MT	4-6-0	1943	Der	1965	MRC (50)	Restoration

*Name carried in preservation.

LMS Stanier 'Jubilee' class 4-6-0 No 5690 Leander pictured on the occasion of a 2005 visit to Crewe Works, also sporting LMS livery and number.

LMS Stanier 'Jubilee' class designed by Stanier for the LMS was built between 1934 and 1936 at Derby (10), North British Locomotive Works, Glasgow (50) and Crewe (131), 191 built in total. The class was allocated the BR number sequence 45552 to 45742 and all of the locos carried names. The need of the LMS for this type of engine was so serious that the first batch was ordered straight off the drawing board without any prototype being built, or running trials taking place. The first Jubilee to be scrapped was No 45637 Windward Islands, which was involved in the tragic Harrow and Wealdstone crash in 1952 and damaged beyond repair. BR began withdrawing the locos in 1960 and only eight examples survived into 1966. Power Classification 6P5F, Driving Wheel 6ft 9in, Cylinders three.

Number	Name	Class	Type	Ex Works	Builder	Ex BR	Location	Status 2009
45593	Kolhapur	6P5F	4-6-0	1934	NB	1967	Tyseley Loco Works	Rebuild
45596	Bahamas	6P5F	4-6-0	1935	NB	1966	K&WVR (95)	Static display
45690	Leander	6P5F	4-6-0	1936	Crw	1964	ELR (109)	Operational
45699	Galatea	6P5F	4-6-0	1936	Crw	1964	WCRC Carnforth	Restoration

LMS numbers 5593, 5596, 5690, and 5699 respectively.

LMS Stanier 'Jubilee' class 4-6-0 No 5593 Kolhapur with LMS livery and number.

LMS Stanier 'Jubilee' class 4-6-0 No 45596 Bahamas (with double chimney) is pictured in the snow at the East Lancashire Railway. *Sue Langston*

LMS Fowler/Stanier 'Royal Scot' class was designed by Fowler for the LMS. They were originally built between 1927 and 1930 by the North British Locomotive Co Ltd (51) and Derby Works (20), 71 locomotives in total. They were allocated the BR number series 46100 to 46170 and all carried names. The first of the powerful parallel boiler Royal Scot locomotives was outshopped by the NBL Co in July 1927, the class leader 6100* Royal Scot hauled the first Royal Scot train on 26 September 1927. It is a widely held belief that 6100 Royal Scot went on a 11,194-mile tour of North America in 1933. Not so, in reality sister engine 6152* The Kings, Dragoon Guardsman undertook that trip. Furthermore the two locomotives never resumed their own identities

LMS Fowler/Stanier rebuilt 'Royal Scot' 4-6-0 No 46115 Scots Guardsman is pictured at the West Coast Railway Co Ltd Carnforth depot immediately following a 2008 major rebuild. *Fred Kerr.*

46115 Scots Guardsman is pictured in LMS lined black livery in 1980.

afterwards. Between 1943 and 1955 the whole class was rebuilt to a Stanier specification incorporating taper boilers, double chimneys and new cylinders. The locos were fitted with smoke deflectors from 1947 onwards. The two preserved examples are representative of the 'rebuilt' type. The last year of operation for the (by then) remaining five locos from the class was 1964. Power Classification 6P as built reclassified to 7P in 1951. Driving Wheel 6ft 9in, Cylinders three.
*LMS number.

Number	Name	Class	Type	Ex Works	Builder	Ex BR	Location	Status 2009
46100	Royal Scot	7P	4-6-0	1930	Der	1962	Bressingham	Operational
46115	Scots Guardsman	7P	4-6-0	1927	NB	1965	WCRC Carnforth	Operational

LMS numbers 6100 and 6115 respectively.

LMS Stanier 'Princess Royal' class 4-6-2 No 46201 Princess Elizabeth gleams in the sunshine as 'she' waits to join the Rocket 150 celebrations.

LMS Stanier 'Princess Royal' class designed by Stanier for the LMS consisted of 13 locomotives built at Crewe between 1933 and 1935. They were allocated the BR number series 46200 to 46212 and all of the engines carried names. The appearance of 6200* 'The Princess Royal' in June 1933 heralded a new high speed era for the LMS and their services on the West Coast main line. It is a widely held belief that while designing this class Stanier drew on the knowledge he had gained while working for the Great Western Railway, with his inspiration being that company's successful four-cylinder 'King Class'. The first of the class to be withdrawn was 46202 Princess Anne, that loco having been damaged beyond repair in the tragic accident at Harrow on 8 October 1952; all were taken out of service before the end of 1962. Power Classification 8P, Driving Wheel 6ft 6in, Cylinders four.
*LMS number.

Number	Name	Class	Type	Ex Works	Builder	Ex BR	Location	Status 2009
46201	Princess Elizabeth	8P	4-6-2	1933	Crw	1962	ELR (109)	Operational
46203	Princess Margaret Rose	8P	4-6-2	1935	Crw	1962	MRC (50)	Stored o/u

LMS numbers 6201 and 6203 respectively.

LMS Stanier 'Princess Royal' class 4-6-2 No 46203 Princess Margaret Rose is pictured in BR service leaving Carstairs Junction with a Birmingham-Glasgow Central service. *David Anderson*

LMS Stanier 'Princess Coronation/Duchess' class, designed by Stanier for the LMS and built at Crewe between 1937 and 1948. They were allocated the BR numbers 46220 to 46257 and all of the engines carried names. In 1935 the London & North Eastern Railway (LNER) introduced a batch of streamlined Class A4 locomotives to operate on their prestigious high-speed London to Scotland services along the East Coast main line. In answer to this challenge the LMS reacted by building the Princess Coronation Class of four-cylinder Pacifics with which to operate their London to Scotland express services.

The LMS sent a complete streamlined Coronation Scot train to tour the USA in 1938 but the outbreak of WWII meant that the loco and coaches were stranded there until 1943. The tour was undertaken by 6229* 'Duchess of Hamilton' in the guise of 6220* Coronation, as that engine was not made available for the tour. From the total of 38 built, 24 locos left the works as streamliners but only three locos came into BR stock with streamlining, and they were all rebuilt by the end of 1949. A BR decree called for all the class to be taken out of service by 31 December 1954. Power Classification 7P as built, reclassified to 8P in 1951. Driving Wheel 6ft 9in, Cylinders four.

LMS Stanier 'Princess Coronation/Duchess' class 4-6-2 No 46325 City of Birmingham is now entombed in the City of Birmingham Museum. The Stanier Pacific is pictured here at Euston Station in BR service. *David Anderson.*

LMS Stanier 'Princess Coronation/Duchess' class 4-6-2 No 46229 en-route to Holyhead with a North Wales Coast Express working in 1991.

Number	Name	Class	Type	Ex Works	Builder	Ex BR	Location	Status 2009
46229	Duchess of Hamilton	8P	4-6-2	1938	Crw	1964	NRM Tyseley	Rebuilt as Streamlined
46233	Duchess of Sutherland	8P	4-6-2	1938	Crw	1964	MRC (50)	Operational
46235	City of Birmingham	8P	4-6-2	1939	Crw	1964	Birmingham Museum	Static display

LMS numbers 6229, 6233 and 6235 respectively.

LMS Stanier 'Princess Coronation/Duchess' class 4-6-2 No 6233 Duchess of, pictured on the Isle of Anglesey during Royal train duty.

LMS Ivatt 2-6-0 No 46443 on main line duty. Pictured in 1987 crossing the Mawwddach Estuary with a Red Dragon working.

LMS Ivatt 2-6-0 a class of 'Mogul' style lightweight locomotives for the LMS designed by Ivatt and introduced between 1946 and 1953. They were built at Darlington (38) Swindon (25) and Crewe (65) a total of 128 locos. They were allocated the BR number series 46400 to 46527. In the years that immediately followed WWII, the LMS was short of lightweight designs needed for use on weight-restricted secondary and branch lines. Those routes had hitherto relied on the older stock of small locomotives which by 1946, were well past their best.

The new 'Class 2' tender locomotives were built with labour-saving in mind, and crews enjoyed the provision of rocking grates, self-emptying ash pans, self-cleaning smokeboxes and side-window cabs. To facilitate reverse running in the absence of turntables on many secondary lines, the tender cab and bunker were designed to give the crews good vision. The engines were very successful and were not confined to LMS territory; five went to the Eastern Region, 13 to the North Eastern Region and 25 to the Western Region. The first of the class to be withdrawn was No 46407 in 1961, with 39 lasting until 1967. No 46417 (LMS 6417) was the last LMS locomotive built at Crewe. The class has proved ideal for use on preserved railways. Power Classification 2MT, Driving Wheel 5ft 0in, Cylinders outside.

Number	Name	Class	Type	Ex Works	Builder	Ex BR	Location	Status 2009
46428		2MT	2-6-0	1948	Crw	1966	ELR (109)	Restoration
46441		2MT	2-6-0	1950	Crw	1967	RSR (114)	Static display
46443		2MT	2-6-0	1950	Crw	1967	SVR (59)	Operational
46447		2MT	2-6-0	1950	Crw	1966	BRC (16)	Restoration
46464		2MT	2-6-0	1950	Crw	1966	Private site Brechin	Restoration
46512	E. V. Cooper, Engineer*	2MT	2-6-0	1952	Sdn	1966	Strasp (108)	Rebuild
46521	Blossom*	2MT	2-6-0	1953	Sdn	1966	GCR (49)	Rebuild

*Name carried in preservation

LMS Ivatt 2-6-0 No 46443 with a demonstration freight train.

LMS Ivatt 2-6-0 No 46512 is pictured on the Strathspey Railway. *Sue Langston*

LMS & SDJR Fowler 'Jinty' 0-6-0 No 16440 (BR number 47279) pictured at the K&WVR double heading with the railway's Fowler 0-6-0. The number carried is from the series 16400 to 16764 which some of the class carried prior pre 1934.

MS & SDJR Fowler 'Jinty' 0-6-0 No 7383 (BR number 47383) looks perfect in this suburban LMS stopping train recreation at the SVR.

LMS & SDJR Fowler 'Jinty' is a class of tank locomotives which became the standard shunting design for the LMS, this class was a development by Fowler of the earlier Johnson Midland Railway design. Reportedly Fowler Class 3F locos were known as Jinties after an engine of this type appeared in the Rev W Awdry's Railway Series book 'The Eight Famous Engines', named Jinty). A total of 415 of the class were built for the LMS and further seven for the S&DJR. They were allocated the BR number series 47260 to 47681 and introduced between 1924 and 1931. The majority of the class were built by outside contractors, Vulcan Foundry Ltd, North British Locomotive Co Ltd, Hunslet Engine Co Ltd, WG Bagnall Ltd, Beardmore Ltd, also LMS Horwich constructed a batch of 15 locos. The LMS took into stock 412 in January 1948 and another five locos, which returned from war service, were added to that number during the year. Power Classification 3F, Driving Wheel 4ft 7in, Cylinders inside.

Number	Name	Class	Type	Ex Works	Builder	Ex BR	Location	Status 2009
47279		3F	0-6-0T	1924	VF	1966	K&WVR (95)	Rebuild
47298		3F	0-6-0T	1924	HE	1966	LR (80)	Operational
47324		3F	0-6-0T	1926	NB	1966	ELR (109)	Operational
47327		3F	0-6-0T	1926	NB	1966	MRC (50)	Operational
47357		3F	0-6-0T	1926	NB	1966	MRC (50)	Rebuild
47383		3F	0-6-0T	1926	VF	1967	SVR (59)	Static display
47406		3F	0-6-0T	1926	VF	1966	GCR (49)	Restoration
47445		3F	0-6-0T	1927	HE	1966	MRC (50)	Restoration
47493		3F	0-6-0T	1928	VF	1966	SpVa (15)	Operational
47564		2F	0-6-0T	1928	HE	1965	MRC (50)	Static display

LMS Stanier 2-8-0 No 8233 is pictured on the 200ft span of the Victoria Bridge on the SVR. The 200ft cast iron span over the river Severn was completed in 1861.

LMS Stanier 2-8-0 is a Stanier-designed freight locomotive introduced by the LMS between 1935 and 1946. They were constructed by contractors Beyer-Peacock (50) North British Locomotive Co (208) and Vulcan Foundry Ltd (67) and at BR Works at Ashford (14) Brighton (93) Darlington (53) Doncaster (50) Eastleigh (23) Horwich (75) Swindon (80) and Crewe (136), in total 849 of the class were built. BR number series 48000 to 48775.

WWII saw the 8Fs pressed into intensive service not only at home but also overseas, and the Stanier 8F became Britain's 'engine of war'. The Government ordered that 208 of the engines be constructed by

LMS Stanier 2-8-0 No 48151 arrives at Crewe Works in the company of preserved LNER B1 61264, on the occasion of the 2005 Great Gathering.

Beyer Peacock & Co Ltd and the North British Locomotive Co Ltd, also requisitioning a further 51 from the LMS, they then shipped the whole batch overseas. Several were lost at sea aboard torpedoed ships but the majority made it to the Middle East and, after being converted to oil burners, they served on vital supply routes ranging as far afield as the Soviet Union.

The 8F freight locos were found to ride well at speed and many were consequently used on passenger trains regularly running at speeds of up to 60mph. The Stanier design was hailed a winner right from the moment that the first example went into traffic. A total of 666 engines eventually came into BR stock. There were 150 Stanier 8Fs in service as 1968, and the end of steam dawned. Power Classification 8F, Driving Wheel 4ft 8½in, Cylinders outside.

LMS Stanier 2-8-0 No 48431 is pictured at the K&WVR in the company of Jinty 47279 and BR Standard 2MT 78022.

Number	Name	Class	Type	Ex Works	Builder	Ex BR	Location	Status 2009
48151		8F	2-8-0	1942	Crw	1968	WCRC Carnforth	Operational
48173		8F	2-8-0	1943	Crw	1965	CVR (44)	Restoration
48305		8F	2-8-0	1943	Crw	1968	GCR (49)	Operational
48431		8F	2-8-0	1944	Sdn	1964	K&WVR (95)	Static display
48518*		8F	2-8-0	1944	Don	1965	Barry (72)	N/A
48624		8F	2-8-0	1943	Asfd	1965	Peak (55)	Restoration
48773**		8F	2-8-0	1940	NB	1963	SVR	Static display

*Donor loco, boiler used for GWR No 1014 new build.   ** War Department engine returned to BR in 1957.

LNWR 'G2 Super D' freight locomotives are synonymous with the name of LNWR engineer Charles Bowen-Cooke, however the class were in the main rebuilds of an earlier Webb design for that company. The locos were built at Crewe Works between 1921 and 1922. The total taken into stock by BR was 60 engines which were allocated the number series 49395 to 49454. During the 1920s loco crews had become used to calling every 0-8-0 engine with a large boiler a 'D'. After 1912 the practice of using Superheating in boiler design gave rise to the term 'Super', hence these large-boilered Superheated 0-8-0s became known as 'Super Ds'. Power Classification 7F, Driving Wheel 4ft 5½in, Cylinders inside.

Restored National Collection ex LNWR/LMS 'G2 Super D' freight locomotive No 49395 is pictured at the Churnet Valley Railway. *David Gibson.*

Number	Name	Class	Type	Ex Works	Builder	Ex BR	Location	Status 2009
49395		7F	0-8-0	1921	Crw	1959	NRM (tours)	Operational

LYR Aspinall Class '5' was introduced by the Lancashire and Yorkshire Railway between 1889 and 1911 and 330 of them were built. BR inherited 109 of the type in January 1948 but immediately scrapped nine of them, BR number series 50621 to 50899. They were almost all withdrawn during the first 10 years of BR's existence however the last example (50746) survived until February 1962. Power Classification 2P, Driving Wheel 5ft 8in, Cylinders inside.

Number	Name	Class	Type	Ex Works	Builder	Ex BR	Location	Status 2009
50621		2P	2-4-2T	1889	Hor	1954	NRM York	Static display

LYR Aspinall Pug 'Class 21' No 51218 is 'filled to overflowing' during a visit to the ELR.

LYR Aspinall Pug 'Class 21' is a design of over 50 diminutive Saddle Tanks built at Horwich Works for the L &Y between 1891 and 1910. BR inherited 23 of the Dock Shunters and placed them in the number series 51202 to 51253. No coal bunkers were fitted with fuel being carried inside the cabs. They were constructed with disc wheels (covered in slide bars) and were fitted with dumb (wooden) buffers. Power Classification 0F, Driving Wheel 3ft 0⅜ in, Cylinders outside.

Number	Name	Class	Type	Ex Works	Builder	Ex BR	Location	Status 2009
51218		0F	0-6-0ST	1901	Hor	1964	K&WVR (95)	Rebuild

LYR Barton Wright Class '25' were designer Barton-Wright's standard 0-6-0 design for the Lancashire & Yorkshire Railway. The class was built by contractors Beyer Peacock Ltd and Vulcan Foundry Ltd between 1876 and 1887. BR inherited 25 of the class and they were allocated the number series 52016 to 52064, no examples survived in service beyond 1959. Power Classification 2F, Driving Wheel 4ft 6in, Cylinders inside.

Number	Name	Class	Type	Ex Works	Builder	Ex BR	Location	Status 2009
52044		2F	0-6-0	1887	BP	1959	K&WVR (95)	Operational

LYR Aspinall Class '27' were designed by Aspinall for the LYR and introduced between 1889 and 1918. BR inherited 245 of the class with none surviving beyond 1962, they were allocated the number series 52088 to 52529. Power Classification 3F, Driving Wheel 5ft 1in, Cylinders inside.

Number	Name	Class	Type	Ex Works	Builder	Ex BR	Location	Status 2009
52322		3F	0-6-0	1895	Hor	1960	ELR (109)	Operational

S&DJR Fowler 2-8-0 as LMS No 13809, S&DJR number was 89 and BR number 53809.

SDJR Fowler 2-8-0 was designed by Fowler and built by the Midland Railway for the Somerset & Dorset Joint Railway at Derby in 1914 and by contractors Robert Stephenson & Co Ltd in 1925. BR inherited 11 examples which carried the number series 53800 to 53810. The class spent the whole of their working lives on the steeply graded S&DJR. Power Classification 7F, Driving Wheel 4ft 8½ in, Cylinders outside.

Left: S&DJR Fowler 2-8-0 as S&DJR No 88 pictured during a visit to the SVR. This loco was LMS number 13808 and BR number 53808.

Number	Name	Class	Type	Ex Works	Builder	Ex BR	Location	Status 2009
53808		7F	2-8-0	1925	RS	1964	WSR (39)	Operational
53809		7F	2-8-0	1925	RS	1964	MRC (50)	Operational

CR McIntosh Class '439' consisted of 79 engines built between 1900 and 1922 at St Rollox Works for the Caledonian Railway; the last 10 of the class were built by Pickersgill and varied slightly from the others. A number of the locos were later fitted with stovepipe chimneys. BR inherited 76 of the class and they were allocated the numbers series 55159 to 55236, none survived in service beyond 1962. Power Classification 2P, Driving Wheel 5ft 9in, Cylinders inside.

Left: CR McIntosh Class '439' No 55189 pictured in BR service at Polmadie shed, April 1956 just prior to preservation. *David Anderson.*

Number	Name	Class	Type	Ex Works	Builder	Ex BR	Location	Status 2009
55189		2P	0-4-4T	1907	SRlx	1962	Bness (103)	Operational

CX Caledonian Railway 0-6-0 is pictured prior to preservation at Corkerhill Shed, Glasgow in 1955. David Anderson

CR McIntosh Class '812' was a McIntosh development of the earlier '57230' class, introduced by the Caledonian Railway between 1899 and 1900. They were allocated the BR number series 57550 to 57628. BR inherited 76 of the class and 10 survived to work in 1963, but none beyond that year. Power Classification 3F, Driving Wheel 5ft 0in, Cylinders inside.

Number	Name	Class	Type	Ex Works	Builder	Ex BR	Location	Status 2009
57566		3F	0-6-0	1899	SRlx	1963	Strasp (108)	Operational

North London Railway 0-6-0T designed by Park, 30 of these engines were built at Bow Works for the North London Railway between 1880 and 1905. Only 15 of the class came into BR stock in 1948 with one being withdrawn without ever receiving a new number, they were allocated the number series 58850 to 58863.

The short wheelbase locos were ideal for Dock shunting work. Several of the class were transferred in 1930 from the NLR to the High Peak & Cromford Railway, from where the last was withdrawn in 1960. Power Classification 2F, Driving Wheel 4ft 4in, Cylinders outside.

Number	Name	Class	Type	Ex Works	Builder	Ex BR	Location	Status 2009
58850		2F	0-6-0T	1880	Bow	1960	Bbell (2)	Rebuild

LNWR Webb 'Coal tank' was a tank engine version of the Webb '58320' Class coal engine and some 300 of the class were built at Crewe between 1881 and 1896. They were useful and popular engines which found their way all over the railway network, in later years some were fitted for push-pull working. BR inherited 64 of the engines in 1948 but scrapped six before allocating them new numbers, BR number series 58880 to 58937. None of the class operated beyond 1958. Power Classification 2F, Driving Wheel 4ft 5½in, Cylinders inside.

Right: **LNWR Webb 0-6-2T 'Coal tank' No 1054 (LMS number 58926) is pictured at the K&WVR in 1986.**

Number	Name	Class	Type	Ex Works	Builder	Ex BR	Location	Status 2009
58926*		2F	0-6-2T	1888	Crw	1958	K&WVR (95)	Rebuild

*LNWR number 1054

Highland Railway Jones Goods a design for the Highland Railway built by Sharp Stewart & Co Ltd. Pictured leaving Carstairs Junction for Auchinleck in June 1963. Double heading with unpreserved loco 57581, that loco withdrawn in November 1963 and cut up.
David Anderson

CR Single No 123, a Drummond design built by Neilson & Co for the Caledonian Railway in 1886. Pictured at Queensferry Junction with an enthusiasts' trip.
David Anderson.

HR Jones Goods a design for the Highland Railway built by Sharp Stewart & Co Ltd in 1894. The 15 engines in the class were history makers as when introduced they were the first 4-6-0 types to appear in Britain. At the time they were reportedly the most powerful main line engines in the country, although freight locos they were often successfully utilised on passenger services.

No 103 (then LMS 17916) was set aside for preservation in 1934. However in 1959 the engine was restored to full working order and rostered to work special trains before being permanently retired. HR 103 is the only surviving ex Highland Railway steam locomotive. Power Classification 4F, Driving Wheel 5ft 3in, Cylinders outside.

Number	Name	Class	Type	Ex Works	Builder	Ex BR	Location	Status 2009
103*		4F	4-6-0	1894	SS	1965	Glasgow Museum	Static display

*HR number, LMS number 17916.

CR Single is a Drummond design built by Neilson & Co for the Caledonian Railway in 1886. The locomotive is a one-off built for the Edinburgh Exhibition in 1886. It then came into the possession of the Caledonian Railway. It was the only single wheeler to ever work in Scotland and the loco turned in some great performances during the famous 1888 'Race to Scotland' rivalry between the East and West Coast Routes. It was withdrawn in 1935 and cosmetically restored but in 1958 it was given a complete overhaul in order to work enthusiasts' special trains. The single wheeler was finally retired in 1965. Power Classification 1P, Driving Wheel 7ft 0in, Cylinders inside.

Number	Name	Class	Type	Ex Works	Builder	Ex BR	Location	Status 2009
123*		1P	4-2-2	1886	N	1965*	Glasgow Museum	Static display

*First withdrawn in 1935 it was refurbished and reinstated in 1958 in order to work specials. LMS number 14010.

NEW BUILD
WORK IN PROGRESS

The three-cylinder LMS Patriot class was introduced towards the end of Sir Henry Fowler's reign as CME of the LMS. The Patriots were a small boilered version of the Royal Scot. All were originally painted out in LMS crimson lake livery with pale yellow and black lining and carried 'LMS' lettering on the tenders. From 1946 most were repainted in LMS lined black with straw and maroon lining. Some Patriots kept this style of livery in the early BR days, with the name British Railways being written in full on the tender. All of the class were later painted out in British Railways standard Brunswick green with orange and black lining, with the BR 'lion and wheel' logo (or later BR crest) on the tender. Between 1946 and 1949 18 of the class were rebuilt to an Ivatt design; gaining a 7P rating they were very similar in appearance to the rebuilt Royal Scots. The class was withdrawn over a two-year period between 1960 and 1962, none were preserved. Based at the Llangollen Railway the 'LMS-Patriot Company Ltd' has been formed with the intention of creating a new 4-6-0 'Patriot Class' locomotive, in the style of the original build.

Based at the Llangollen Railway the 'LMS-Patriot Company Ltd' has been formed with the intention of creating a new 4-6-0 'Patriot Class' locomotive, in the style of the original build. Unpreserved Patriot 4-6-0 No 45541 Duke of Sutherland is seen at Rugby Midland Station in BR service, August 1960.

Number	Name	Class	Type	Start date	Builder	Donor loco(s)	Location	Status 2009
45551*	The Unknown Warrior	6P5F	4-6-0	2008	LMS Patriot Co Ltd		LR (80)	Work in progress

*Not a BR number or name

Stanier Princess Royal Class 4-6-2 No 6201 'Princess Elizabeth' (BR number 46201), built at Crewe in 1933, became a record breaker on 16 November 1936 when it covered the London Euston-Glasgow Central journey in a time of five hours 53 minutes and 38 seconds. With a seven-coach train 6201 recorded an average speed of 68.2mph. Locomotive 6201 served the LMS from 1933 until 1948 and thereafter British Railways until withdrawn from service in October 1962. The preserved locomotive completed a commemorative Crewe-Glasgow round trip on 11/12 November 2006, the 70th anniversary of the record run. Princess Elizabeth is pictured soon after arriving at Glasgow Central on that occasion.

Even under leaden skies Ex LMS Princess Coronation 4-6-2 No 6233 Duchess of Sutherland makes a fine sight as 'she' hurries past Beeston Castle with an outward Welsh Dragon (Crewe-Holyhead-Crewe) in June 2005.

EX BR LNER
LOCOMOTIVES

I n 1948 the newly formed British Railways took into stock 6548 ex LNER steam locomotives, many built by the 11 pre-grouping companies which were brought together to form the LNER. The Eastern Region and North Eastern Region of BR utilised steam locomotive numbers in the series 60001 to 69999.

By the end of 1960 the total of ex LNER steam locomotives in service had reduced to 2866 and tellingly to only 111 by the end of 1966. No ex LNER

operational locomotives worked through into the last year of BR steam but two service locomotives (stationary boilers) did continue in BR use beyond 1967.

Preserved ex BR LNER type locomotives total only 37 examples; it is the lowest total of rescued steam engines from any of the pre-nationalisation railway companies. In addition a 'new build' project was completed in 2008 thus adding a replica A1 4-6-2 to that number.

On top of the world. Mighty A4 Pacific 4498 Sir Nigel Gresley (LNER 60007) is pictured whilst on Settle & Carlisle main line excursion duty in 1985.

Above: Now in the USA A4 4-6-2 No 60008 Dwight D. Eisenhower is pictured in BR service at Grantham in 1955.

Left: No 60007 Sir Nigel Gresley is pictured in the winter snow at the East Lancashire Railway.

Below: Now in Canada A4 4-6-2 No 60010 Dominion of Canada is pictured in snowy BR service at Doncaster in 1963.

Ancient and Modern. A4 Pacific No 60009 is seen at Carlisle Station while on main line duty. The 1937-built steam loco is pictured with a modern 'Class 67' diesel and 'Virgin Pendelino'. *David Gibson*

Preserved A4 No 60009 is pictured leaving Chester with a North Wales Coast Express service in 1991 while masquerading as 'her' unpreserved sister loco No 60027 Merlin.

A4 Steamlined Pacific locomotives were a Gresley design of express passenger engines for the London & North Eastern Railway; all were built at Doncaster between 1935 and 1938. The 34 streamlined locomotives carried the BR numbers series 60001 to 60034 and all were named. The first A4 (which was a development of the previously successful A3 design) was 60014 Silver Link and it emerged from Doncaster Works in 1935. The first four built 2509-2512 (LNER numbers) were given a silver livery and hauled the 'Silver Jubilee' train between London and Newcastle, a journey they completed in less than four hours.

The engines regularly proved themselves in service on the fast heavy express trains of the East Coast main line, frequently running at speeds of around 100mph. BR took into stock all 34 A4s making the first withdrawals from service in 1962, none of the class continued in use beyond September 1966. Power Classification 7P as introduced, reclassified to 8P in 1951. Driving Wheel 6ft 8in, Cylinders three.

Number	Name	Class	Type	Ex Works	Builder	Ex BR	Location	Status 2009
60007	Sir Nigel Gresley	A4	4-6-2	1937	Don	1966	NYMR (99)	Operational
60008	Dwight D. Eisenhower	A4	4-6-2	1937	Don	1963	NRM USA	Static display
60009	Union of South Africa	A4	4-6-2	1937	Don	1965	Thornton	Operational
60010	Dominion of Canada	A4	4-6-2	1937	Don	1965	NRM Canada	Static display
60019	Bittern	A4	4-6-2	1937	Don	1966	MHants (11)	Operational
60022	Mallard*	A4	4-6-2	1938	Don	1963	NRM York	Static display

*Mallard is the holder of the world speed record for steam locomotives at 126mph (202.7km/h). The record was achieved on 3 July, 1938. 60022 (4468) is a part of the National Collection.
LNER numbers 60007 – 4498, 60008 – 4496, 60009 – 4488, 60010 – 4489, 60019 – 4464 and 60022 – 4468.

A3 Pacific Flying Scotsman with LNER number and German-style smoke deflectors seen at Seamer during York-Scarborough services in July 2004, on the occasion of the loco's first run after becoming part of the National Collection. *Brian Sharpe*

A3 4-6-2 Gresley Pacific locomotives taken into BR stock totalled 79 and included No 4472 'Flying Scotsman' (BR number 60103) which is arguably the most famous steam locomotive in the world, the total being made up of 78 A3s and one A10 No 60068 which was in 1948 converted to an A3. From 1928 a total of 26 engines were built new as A3 types while the rest were originally A1s and then A10s, subsequently rebuilt as A3s between 1927 and 28. The BR number series of the class was 60035 to 60112, they were built at Doncaster Works (engines 60035-60063 and 60084-60112) and North British Locomotive Company Glasgow (engines 60064-60083) all carried names. The class served the LNER and then BR well with withdrawals starting in 1958, 59 of the class remained in service at the beginning of 1963; the last to be withdrawn was 60052 in January 1966. Flying Scotsman was bought 'out of service' for preservation in 1963 and after a long period in private ownership(s) it became part of the national collection in 2004. Power Classification 7P, Driving Wheel 6ft 8in, Cylinders three.

Number	Name	Class	Type	Ex Works	Builder	Ex BR	Location	Status 2009
60103*	Flying Scotsman	A3	4-6-2	1923	Don	1963	NRM York	Operational

*LNER number, 4472 currently carried.

A3 Pacific Flying Scotsman with BR number 60103; seen when in private ownership during a visit to the Llangollen Railway during 1995.

In September 1990 Flying Scotsman is seen as 4472 during a visit to the Severn Valley Railway, but without smoke deflectors.

A2 4-6-2 locomotives were designed by Thompson for the LNER with the final 15 from the class of 40 engines being redesigned by Peppercorn his successor in 1946, the class carried the BR numbers 60500 to 60539. The origin of the class is varied with the first of the A2s being rebuilds of the earlier Gresley 2-8-2 'P2' locomotives, reclassified A2/2 after conversion. The next four engines built in 1944 were originally ordered as V2 2-6-2s but were redesigned and built as Pacific locos although retaining their V2 boilers, they were classified A2/1. There followed Thompson's new Pacific design classified as A2/3 of which 30 were ordered but only 15 built before his retirement. Peppercorn then redesigned and oversaw the building of the outstanding 15 locos (60525 to 60539) which were classified A2. Preserved example 60532 is a 'Peppercorn' engine and part of the North Eastern Locomotive Preservation Group's collection. Power Classification 7MT, Driving Wheel 6ft 2in, Cylinders three.

Left: **Peppercorn A2 4-6-2 locomotive No 60532 Blue Peter at Appleby during Settle & Carlisle main line duty.** *David Gibson.*

Number	Name	Class	Type	Ex Works	Builder	Ex BR	Location	Status 2009
60532	Blue Peter	A2	4-6-2	1948	Don	1966	Darlington North Road Museum	Static display

V2 2-6-2 locomotives were designed by Gresley for the LNER and entered service between 1936 and 1944. The class of 184 engines carried the BR number series 60800 to 60983 with only eight of the class being named; Darlington built 164 engines and Doncaster the remaining 20. The preserved example Green Arrow was so named to promote a special fast freight service. All of the class entered BR service and withdrawals commenced in 1962, 14 locos survived in service into 1966 but none beyond. 'Green Arrow' is a National Collection loco. Power Classification 6MT, Driving Wheel 6ft 2in, Cylinders three.

Right: **Gresley V2 2-6-2 LNER No 4471 Green Arrow is pictured during a 2007 visit to the North Yorkshire Moors Railway.** *David Gibson.*

Number	Name	Class	Type	Ex Works	Builder	Ex BR	Location	Status 2009
60800*	Green Arrow	V2	2-6-2	1936	Don	1962	NRM	Static display

*LNER number 4771

Thompson B1 4-6-0 No 61264 (BR Number) is pictured during a visit to the Churnet Valley Railway, in BR lined black livery.

Thompson B1 4-6-0 No 1264 (LNER number) is pictured during a visit to the Great Central Railway, in LNER livery

B1 4-6-0 design was Thompson's first for the LNER. They carried the BR number series 61000 to 61409 and were built by Darlington, North British Locomotive Co Ltd, and Vulcan Foundry Ltd. In 1948 BR took into stock 342 locos with building still under way, the highest number in service with BR rose to 409. Loco No 61057 was scrapped in 1950 following a collision at Chelmsford and wholesale withdrawals were made from 1961 onwards. In January 1967 only 27 B1s remained

on the books and none survived beyond that year. Loco No 61306 has been preserved with the name Mayflower which was originally carried by No 61379. The other preserved example loco No 61264 was transferred from operational engine to service loco, as service stock number 29, in December 1965 and was finally withdrawn from all uses in July 1967. Power Classification 5MT, Driving Wheel 6ft 2in, Cylinders outside.

Number	Name	Class	Type	Ex Works	Builder	Ex BR	Location	Status 2009
61264		B1	4-6-0	1947	NBL	1965	LNWR	Rebuild
61306	Mayflower	B1	4-6-0	1948	NBL	1967	BLR (42)	Operational

Holden B12 4-6-0 No 61572 is pictured stored out of use at the North Norfolk Railway.

B12 4-6-0 locomotives were a Holden design for the Great Eastern Railway introduced between 1911 and 1928 and there were four variants B12/1, B12/2, B12/3 and B12/4. Collectively they carried the number series 61500 to 61580 (with gaps due to earlier scrapping) additionally numbers 61500, 61509, 61510 and 61517 were scrapped, after nationalisation but before the 1949 BR stock list was compiled.

Of the 60 locos inherited by BR 40 were built at Stratford and 20 by Beyer Peacock & Co Ltd. With the exception of the preserved example none of the class survived in service beyond January 1959. Loco No 61572 is a B12/3 variant, from a batch of Gresley rebuilds with larger round-topped boilers. Power Classification 4P, Driving Wheel 6ft 6in, Cylinders inside.

Number	Name	Class	Type	Ex Works	Builder	Ex BR	Location	Status 2009
61572		B12/3	4-6-0	1928	BP	1961	NNR (69)	Stored o/u

THE GREAT MARQUESS – **THREE-CYLINDER GRESLEY MOGUL**

The preserved Great Marquess in LNER guise. No 3442 is pictured with a rake of restored LNER teak coaches at the Severn Valley Railway.

K4 2-6-0 class was introduced by the LNER especially to work the West Highland Line in Scotland. The three-cylinder 2-6-0 (Mogul) is a Gresley design introduced between 1937 and 1939, and built at Darlington.

There were six locomotives built, all were named, BR number series 61993 to 61998. All remained in BR service into 1961, but not beyond. Power Classification 6MT, Driving Wheel 5ft 2in, Cylinders three.

Number	Name	Class	Type	Ex Works	Builder	Ex BR	Location	Status 2009
61994*	The Great Marquess	K4	2-6-0	1938	Dar	1961	Thornton Tours	Operational

*LNER number 3442.

The Great Marquess in BR service. No 61994 is pictured with a Fife-Glasgow stopping train at North Queensferry. *David Anderson*

The preserved Great Marquess in BR guise. No 61994 with BR lined black livery at the Severn Valley Railway. *Sue Langston*

K1 2-6-0 class of locomotives were developed from the Gresley K4 converted to K1/1 by Peppercorn in 1945. The class of 70 locomotives were introduced between 1949 and 1950 for British Railways and all built by North British Locomotive Co Ltd. In 1965 scrapping reduced the class number to 31 locos and none survived to work beyond 1967. Power Classification 6MT, Driving Wheel 5ft 2in, Cylinders outside.

Left: **Preserved 'K1 Class' 2-6-0 62005 is pictured towards the end of its BR service at Leeds Holbeck in 1967.**

Number	Name	Class	Type	Ex Works	Builder	Ex BR	Location	Status 2009
62005	Lord of the Isles*	K1	2-6-0	1949	NBL	1967	NYMR	Operational

*Name sometimes carried in preservation.

D40 4-4-0 class was designed by Pickersgill for the Great North of Scotland Railway, that railway's 'V' Class'. Due to the company having financial problems they only took delivery of the first five of the 10 ordered, from the builders Neilson Reid & Co, the remaining five being bought by the South East & Chatham Railway Co Ltd. Later other locos of the class were built at Inverurie Works. BR took into stock 18 examples in the number series 62260 to 62279 (number 62263 not allocated). Loco No 62277 Gordon Highlander was the last in service. In 1958 No 62277 was restored and painted in original GNoSR livery outshopped as No 49; in that guise it worked special trains for two years before being retired to Glasgow Museum of Transport. Power Classification 2P as built, reclassified to 1Pin 1953. Driving Wheel 6ft 1in, Cylinders inside.

Ex Great North of Scotland Railway 'V' Class' 4-4-0 No 49 Gordon Highlander (LNER number 62277), which became LNER D40 class, is pictured while on 'Special' duty with an SLS railtour outside Dumfries Shed in June 1959. *David Anderson.*

Number	Name	Class	Type	Ex Works	Builder	Ex BR	Location	Status 2009
62277*	Gordon Highlander	D40	4-4-0	1913	NB	1958	Glasgow Museum	Static display

*Great North of Scotland Railway No 49.

Ex North British Railway 'K Class' Glen (LNER D34 Class) No 256 Glen Douglas (BR 62469) is pictured while hauling an SLS/RCTS 1960 railtour at Queensferry Junction. *David Anderson.*

D34 'Glen' a class of 32 engines designed by Reid and built for the North British Railway as that company's 'K Class' at Cowlairs Works between 1913 and 1920. BR inherited 30 working examples of the class allocating them the number series 62467 to 62498 (62491 not allocated). In April 1959 No 62469 was completely refurbished. It was outshopped in November of that year with NBR livery and the number 256, in order to work railtours. Two years later it was finally withdrawn from service and moved to Glasgow Museum of Transport. Power Classification 3P, Driving Wheel 6ft 0in, Cylinders inside.

Number	Name	Class	Type	Ex Works	Builder	Ex BR	Location	Status 2009
62469	Glen Douglas	D34	4-4-0	1913	Cow	1959	Bness (103)	Static display

*North British Railway No 256.

D11 'Large Director' a class of 35 engines built to a Robinson design at the Gorton Works of the Great Central Railway. The class entered service between 1920 and 1924 and were heavier versions of the earlier GCR 'D10 Class'. They were allocated the BR numbers 62660 to 62694. They were built in two batches D11/1 totalling 11 engines and the slightly modified D11/2 variant (for Scottish routes and known as the 'Scottish Directors') of which there were 24 built. The preserved example No 62660 is a D11/1 and part of the national collection. Power Classification 3P, driving wheel 6ft 9in, Cylinders inside.

Preserved D11 'Large Director' 506 Butler Henderson (LNER 2660, BR 62660) is pictured in Great Central Railway livery at the preserved Great Central Railway in 1987.

Number	Name	Class	Type	Ex Works	Builder	Ex BR	Location	Status 2009
62660*	Butler Henderson	D11/2	4-4-0	1919	Gor	1960	NRM	Static display

*LNER number 2660. GCR number 506

D49 'Shire & Hunt' a class of 75 engines designed by Gresley and introduced between 1927 and 1935, with one loco being rebuilt by Thompson in 1942. There were four variants of the class D49/1, D49/2, D49/3 and D49/4, the preserved example loco No 62712 is a D49/1. All 75 entered BR stock but none of the class worked beyond the end of 1961. Power Classification 4P, Driving Wheel 6ft 8in, Cylinders three (preserved example).

Left: D49/1 Shire 4-4-0 No 62712 Morayshire is pictured at the end of its BR life and prior to restoration. Seen at Dalry Road depot Edinburgh waiting to be towed away. *David Anderson.*

Number	Name	Class	Type	Ex Works	Builder	Ex BR	Location	Status 2009
62712	Morayshire	D49/1	4-4-0	1928	Dar	1961	Bness (103)	Operational

E4 2-4-0 class designed by Holden were built for the Great Eastern Railway between 1891 and 1902 and were that company's 'T26 Class'. BR inherited 18 of the class which were allocated the number series 62780 to 62797; they were mostly employed on branch line work in Cambridgeshire and other parts of East Anglia. Power Classification 1MT, Driving Wheel 5ft 8in, Cylinders inside.

Number	Name	Class	Type	Ex Works	Builder	Ex BR	Location	Status 2009
62785*		E4	2-4-0	1891	Str	1959	Bressingham	Static display

*Great Eastern Railway No 490.

Q6 0-8-0 class designed by Raven for the North Eastern Railway as that company's 'T2 Class' was introduced between 1913 and 1921. The first 70 of this 120-strong class were built at Darlington and the last 50 by Armstrong Whitworth & Co Ltd; they carried BR numbers in the series 63340 to 63459. In common with the J27 0-6-0 class these engines had the distinction of being the last pre-grouping locomotives to remain in service. The January 1967 BR stock list showed 17 examples remaining in service, the preserved example became the last to be withdrawn in September 1967. Power Classification 6F, Driving Wheel 4ft 7¼in, Cylinders outside.

Number	Name	Class	Type	Ex Works	Builder	Ex BR	Location	Status 2009
63395		Q6	0-8-0	1918	Dar	1967	NYMR	Operational

Q7 0-8-0 class designed by Raven for the North Eastern Railway as that company's 'T3 Class' was introduced between 1919 and 1924. All 15 locos were built at Darlington and carried BR numbers in the series 63460 to 63474. These three-cylinder engines were similar in appearance to the 'Q6' two-cylinder engines but could be distinguished by the fact that their outside cylinders drove on the second pair of wheels while those of the 'Q6' drove on the third pair of wheels. Power Classification 7F as built, reclassified to 8F in 1953. Driving Wheel 4ft 7¼in, Cylinders three.

Number	Name	Class	Type	Ex Works	Builder	Ex BR	Location	Status 2009
63460		Q7	0-8-0	1919	Dar	1962	NRM Shildon	Static display

04 2-8-0 class introduced between 1911 and 1920, designed by Robinson for the Great Central Railway and classified '8K Class' which later became the LNER '04 Class', built at Gorton Works and by various contractors. They were allocated BR numbers in the series 63570 and 63920. There were originally eight variants of the type and additionally a batch of 58 rebuilds by Thompson (from 1944 onwards) which were reclassified 'O1'. During WWI the class became the Railway Operating Division (ROD) of the Royal Engineers standard type of engine for war service. Accordingly 521 were built especially for service in France. In WWII 92 of these engines were commandeered for war service in the Middle East. In both instances after the conflicts the majority of the locos returned to the UK and were absorbed into the operating stocks of various railway companies, while others remained overseas. BR inherited 278 of the '04' types, and 51 of the rebuilt 'O1' class. The preserved example is an '04/1' variant ie an original design of engine with a small GCR style Belpaire boiler, steam vacuum brakes and a tender water scoop. 04/1 Power Classification, Driving Wheel 4ft 8in, Cylinders outside.

Left: **04/1 Robinson 2-8-0 No 63601 is pictured at home on the preserved Great Central Railway.**

Number	Name	Class	Type	Ex Works	Builder	Ex BR	Location	Status 2009
63601		04/1	2-8-0	1912	Gor	1963	GCR (49)	Operational

J21 0-6-0 were built between 1886 and 1894 for the North Eastern Railway, designed by Worsdell as that company's 'C Class' they were built at Darlington and Gateshead. BR allocated the class numbers in the series 65025 to 65123 (with gaps due to scrapping) and took into stock 83 working examples which by 1951 had reduced to 29 engines. None survived in service beyond the end of 1961. Power Classification 2F, Driving Wheel 5ft 1¼in, Cylinders inside.

Number	Name	Class	Type	Ex Works	Builder	Ex BR	Location	Status 2009
65033		J21	0-6-0	1889	Ghd	1962	NNR (69)	Rebuild

J36 0-6-0 a class built for the North British Railway between 1888 and 1900 to a Holmes design were the NBRs 'C Class', in total 168 were built of which 123 came into BR stock. When introduced they were the most numerous class on the NBR. They were given BR numbers in the series 65210 to 65346 and 11 carried names. Power Classification 2F, Driving Wheel 5ft 0in, Cylinders inside.

Left: LNER 'J36 Class' 0-6-0 ex North British Railway 'C Class' No 65243 Maude is pictured in BR service at Dalmeny Junction in 1957. The engine went to France in WWI and on her return was named in honour of Lt-Gen Sir Frederick Stanley Maude. *David Anderson.*

Number	Name	Class	Type	Ex Works	Builder	Ex BR	Location	Status 2009
65243	Maude	J36	0-6-0	1891	N	1966	Bness (103)	Static display

J15 0-6-0 class introduced between 1883 and 1913 is a type associated with four railway engineers. They were first introduced by Worsdell in 1883 as the Great Eastern Railway 'Y14 Class' and his successors J Holden, SD Holden and Hill continued to build them. The 127 which came into BR stock were all built at Stratford Works; they carried numbers in the BR series 65350 to 65479. These locos were to be seen at work in all parts of East Anglia; furthermore 43 of the class were loaned to the Government and worked overseas during WWI. Power Classification 2F, Driving Wheel 4ft 11in, Cylinders inside.

Left: The LNER J15 0-6-0 class was originally introduced as the Great Eastern Railway 'Y14 Class'. No 65462 is seen at the North Norfolk Railway.

Number	Name	Class	Type	Ex Works	Builder	Ex BR	Location	Status 2009
65462		J15	0-6-0	1912	Str	1962	NNR (69)	Operational

J17 0-6-0 class introduced by Holden for the Great Eastern Railway between 1900 and 1910 as that company's 'G58 Class'. BR took into stock 89 of the class and allocated the locos numbers in the series 65500 to 65589. LNER loco No 8200 was destroyed by a German rocket in 1944 otherwise that loco would have become number 65550, the 90th member of the class. Power Classification 4F, Driving Wheel 4ft 11in, Cylinders inside.

Number	Name	Class	Type	Ex Works	Builder	Ex BR	Location	Status 2009
65567		J17	0-6-0	1905	Str	1962	NRM	Static display

LNER J27 0-6-0 class locomotives were originally North Eastern Railway classified 'P3 Class'. Preserved loco No 65894 is pictured in NER guise as engine No 2392 during a 1992 visit to the Llangollen Railway.

J27 0-6-0 class introduced between 1906 and 1923 were Worsdell/Raven locomotives for the North Eastern Railway classified as NER 'P3 Class'. BR took into stock 115 of the class which were built at Darlington (65), North British Locomotive Co Ltd (20) Beyer Peacock Co Ltd (20) and Robert Stephenson & Co Ltd (10). No 65494 is part of the North Eastern Locomotive Preservation Groups collection of locomotives. Power Classification 4F as built, reclassified to 5F in 1953. Driving Wheel 4ft 7¼ in, Cylinders inside.

Number	Name	Class	Type	Ex Works	Builder	Ex BR	Location	Status 2009
65894*		J27	0-6-0	1923	Dar	1967	Darlington North Road Museum	Static display

*NER number 2392

J94 WD (Ministry of Supply) class was designed by Riddles for the Ministry of Supply and introduced between 1943 and 1946. A vast number of these powerful shunting engines were built by contractors Hudwell Clarke & Co Ltd, WG Bagnall Ltd, Robert Stephenson & Hawthorns Ltd, Hunslet Engine Co Ltd, Andrew Barclay Sons & Co Ltd and Vulcan Foundry Ltd. Many of these versatile engines were purchased out of WD ownership by collieries and heavy industry and it is estimated that over 50 of those (which were never BR stock, but may now carry ex BR numbers) are still operating on preserved railways. The 75 locos of this type taken into LNER stock were classified J94 and all of those were inherited by BR, in the number series 68006 to 68080. Power Classification 4F, Driving Wheel 4ft 3in, Cylinders inside.

Number	Name	Class	Type	Ex Works	Builder	Ex BR	Location	Status 2009
68077		J94	0-6-0ST	1947	AB	1962	SpVa (15)	Stored o/u
68078		J94	0-6-0ST	1946	AB	1963	KESR (9)	Rebuild

Y7 0-4-0T class were originally North Eastern Railway 'H Class' designed by Worsdell. The preserved example was transferred from 'operational' to the status of 'departmental engine' for use at Stratford Works in 1952 as No 34. There is another preserved example NER No 1310 which was sold out of service and never came into BR stock. Power Classification 0F, Driving Wheel 3ft 6¼ in, Cylinders inside.

Number	Name	Class	Type	Ex Works	Builder	Ex BR	Location	Status 2009
68088		Y7	0-4-0T	1923	Dar	1952	NNR (69)	Rebuild

Y9 0-4-0ST class were originally dock yard type shunters built for the North British Railway as that company's 'G Class'; they were designed by Holmes and introduced between 1882 and 1899. The locos of this class became known as 'Pugs'. Power Classification 0F, Driving Wheel 3ft 8in, Cylinders outside.

Left: **Ex North British Railway 'G Class', LNER Y9 0-4-0ST 'Pug' No 68095 is pictured prior to preservation at Seafield Depot, Leith in 1959.** *David Anderson.*

Number	Name	Class	Type	Ex Works	Builder	Ex BR	Location	Status 2009
68095		Y9	0-4-0ST	1887	Cow	1962	Bness (103)	Static display

Y1 0-4-0T class of geared steam locomotives were built by the Sentinel Co for the LNER and intended for use as dock shunters. BR inherited 15 of these engines with single-speed gearboxes which worked at railway yards with tight curves and restricted loading gauge, eg the harbour at Lowestoft. Power Classification 'Unclassified', Driving Wheel 2ft 6in, Cylinders inside.

Number	Name	Class	Type	Ex Works	Builder	Ex BR	Location	Status 2009
68153		Y1	0-4-0T	1933	S	1954	Mton (98)	Stored o/u

J69 0-6-0T class designed for the Great Eastern Railway by Holden were introduced between 1902 and 1904 and were that company's 'S56 Class'. The preserved example was part of a batch of 134 engines which came into BR stock and was made up of J69s and also J27s, a similar design of GER engine. The combined classes were allocated BR numbers in the series 68490 to 68636. There were four variants within the combined classes. The preserved loco is a J69/1, introduced in 1904 as a development of the J67 and subsequently classified J69/1 by BR in 1952. Power Classification 3F (from 1952), Driving Wheel 4ft 0in, Cylinders inside.

Number	Name	Class	Type	Ex Works	Builder	Ex BR	Location	Status 2009
68633		J69/1	0-6-0T	1904	Str	1960	NRM York	Static display

J52 0-6-0ST originated from the Great Northern Railway 'J13 Class' and 132 of the class came into BR stock being allocated numbers in the series 68757 to 68889. The locos were developed as the GNR's standard shunting engine under both Stirling and Ivatt between 1892 and 1897. The preserved example is an Ivatt variant classified J52/2 which was built in 1899 by Sharp Stewart & Co. Power Classification 3F, Driving Wheel 4ft 8in, Cylinders inside.

Number	Name	Class	Type	Ex Works	Builder	Ex BR	Location	Status 2009
68846		J52/2	0-6-0ST	1899	SS	1959	NRM York	Static display

J72 0-6-0T class designed for the North Eastern Railway by Worsdell has a unique claim to fame. The class was in production for 53 years by three different railway companies and during the reign of four different locomotive superintendents, Worsdell, Raven, Gresley and Peppercorn. They were built at Darlington and Doncaster Works and by contractors Armstrong Whitworth Co Ltd. BR took into stock 85 of the class, numbered in the series 68670 to 68754 and 69001 to 69028. Building of the type was continued by BR, as a result of which the number of J72s in service peaked at 113 locos in 1951, however none remained in normal service beyond 1964. Two locos continued until 1966 as service stock, numbered 58 and 59 respectively. Power Classification 2F, Driving Wheel 4ft 1¼in, Cylinders inside.

Number	Name	Class	Type	Ex Works	Builder	Ex BR	Location	Status 2009
69023		J72	0-6-0T	1951	Dar	1964	Darlington North Road Museum	Restoration

Preserved Gresley ex Great Northern Railway N2 0-6-0T No 4744 (BR 69523) is pictured at the preserved Great Central Railway.

N2 0-6-2T designed by Gresley was an enlarged version of the earlier Great Northern Railway 'N1 Class'. The class was introduced between 1920 and 1929 and BR inherited 107 of the type, allocating the locos numbers in the series 69490 to 69596, none survived in service beyond 1962. There were four variants and the preserved example is an N2/2 which was fitted with condensing apparatus during BR use in the London area. Power Classification 3MT, Driving Wheel 5ft 8in, Cylinders inside.

Number	Name	Class	Type	Ex Works	Builder	Ex BR	Location	Status 2009
69523*		N2/2	0-6-2T	1921	NB	1962	GCR (49)	Operational

*This loco appeared in the film The Railway Children as the engine hauling the 'Scots Flyer'. For the occasion it was painted in fictional Great Northern and Southern Railway livery. LNER number 4744.

N7 0-6-2T class was designed for use on suburban services out of London's Liverpool Street Station and first introduced by the Great Eastern Railway in 1914, and then later by the LNER as Gresley developments of the original Hill design. BR took into stock 134 of the class; none survived in service beyond 1962. There were five variants and the preserved example is an N7/4, ie original N7 rebuilt with Gresley round-topped boiler. Power Classification 3MT, Driving Wheel 4ft 10in, Cylinders inside.

Number	Name	Class	Type	Ex Works	Builder	Ex BR	Location	Status 2009
69621		N7/4	0-6-2T	1924	Str	1962	NNR (69)	Operational

▌NEW BUILD

The last of the Peppercorn 'A1' locomotives was scrapped in 1966. The A1 LNER class totalled 50 engines. The locomotives were built by both the LNER and BR between 1948 and 1949. Numbers 60113 to 60129 and 60153 to 60162 were built at Doncaster; the remainder 60130 to 60151 were built at Darlington. The new locomotive is numbered 60163. Tornado made its first public moves in steam during August 2008. *Power Classification 7P when introduced, reclassified to 8P in 1951, Driving Wheel 6ft 8in, Cylinders three. *Original A1 design.

Right: **New build Peppercorn 'A1' 4-6-2 locomotive 60163 pictured during running in trials at the Great Central Railway in 2008.** *Brian Sharpe.*

Number	Name	Class	Type	Ex Works	Builder	Location	Status 2009
60163	Tornado	A1	4-6-2	2008	A1 Trust	GCR (49)	Operational

National Collection locomotive Ex LNER 'V2 Class' 2-6-2 No 60800 Green Arrow pictured at the Churnet Valley Railway. Designed by Gresley this loco was built at Doncaster Works and entered service with the LNER in 1936, it was withdrawn by BR in 1962. *David Gibson*

EX BR SR
LOCOMOTIVES

The January 1948 total of ex Southern Railway steam locomotives taken into stock by British Railways and allocated to the Southern Region of BR was 1851. The locomotives originated from the Southern Railway and the three companies from which it was formed in 1923, at the time of grouping.

The Southern Region of BR utilised steam locomotive numbers in the series 30001 to 30957, 31002 to 31925, 32001 to 32699, 33001 to 33040, 34001 to 34110, and 35001 to 35030. As a general rule BR placed SR ex London & South Western Railway (LSWR) locos in the 30000 series, ex SR London Brighton & South Coast Railway (LBSCR) locos in

the 31000 series and ex SR South Eastern & Chatham Railway (SECR) locos in the 32000 series, but there are several exceptions. Later build SR locos and BR-built Southern Region locos were placed in the 33000, 34000 and 35000 series. The steam locomotives of the Isle of Wight Railway, although administered by the 'Southern', were numbered separately in the series W1 to W36.

Ex Southern locos, of the same class may not be sequentially numbered, for the purpose of this publication ex SR steam locos are listed in BR class order. There are a total of 81 ex BR Southern Region locomotives preserved and one new build project was recorded as being 'work in progress' at the end of 2008.

Ex LSWR 'T9 Class' 4-4-0 is pictured in BR service leaving Padstow with a local service.

David Anderson.

B4 LSWR class designed by Adams and then improved by Drummond between 1891 and 1908 were dock shunting engines of which 14 were named. They mainly worked in Southampton Docks. BR inherited 25 of these locos and allocated them numbers in the series 30081 to 30103 and 30147 to 30176. Several of the class were sold out of service for use by industrial concerns. The last in BR service were the two preserved examples, both withdrawn in 1963, 30102 in September and 30096 October. Power Classification as inherited by BR, 0F, reclassified to 1F in 1953. Driving wheel 3ft 9¾in, Cylinders outside.

Ex LSWR 'B4 Class' 0-4-0T No 30096 Normandy is pictured when in BR service at Eastleigh, in the spring of 1963. The loco is coupled to preserved Stroudley Terrier 32650 and unpreserved 'Q1 Class' 0-6-0 No 33009.

Number	Name	Class	Type	Ex Works	Builder	Ex BR	Location	Status 2009
30096	Normandy	B4	0-4-0T	1893	9Elm	1963	Bbell (2)	Static display
30102	Granville	B4	0-4-0T	1893	9Elm	1963	Bressingham	Static display

'Lord Nelson Class' 4-6-0 preserved loco No 30850 Lord Nelson pictured after restoration on Cumbrian Mountain Express duty, in 1985.

LN SR class locomotives were designed to haul the fastest and heaviest express services on the Southern Railway. They were designed by Maunsell and introduced between 1926 and 1929. BR took into stock all 16 locos in the class and allocated them numbers in the series 30850 to 30865, all carried names honouring great naval commanders. When first in service the 'Nelsons' took the title of 'most powerful UK locomotive', previously held by the GWR, that company later claimed the title back following the introduction of the 'King Class'. All 16 locos operated for BR into 1961 but none saw service beyond the end of 1962. The preserved example was one of the last two to be withdrawn, in August 1962. No 30850 is a National Collection engine. Power Classification 6P as introduced reclassified to 7P in 1951. Driving Wheel 6ft 7in, Cylinders four.

Number	Name	Class	Type	Ex Works	Builder	Ex BR	Location	Status 2009
30850*	Lord Nelson	LN	4-6-0	1926	Elh	1962	NRM	Operational

*SR number 850.

'Lord Nelson Class' No 30850 Lord Nelson was withdrawn by BR in August 1962. Still in BR service the loco is seen in charge of a Home Counties Railway Club special at Didcot, in June 1962. *David Anderson.*

M7 LSWR class locomotives designed by Drummond were introduced between 1897 and 1911. BR took into stock 104 of the class and allocated the engines numbers in the series 30021 to 30060, between 30140 and 30481 and 30667 to 30676. The M7s were developed from the Adams 'T1' and 'O2' classes. They were at first tried on express passenger services between Exeter and Plymouth but later relegated to suburban services in the London area following a derailment at speed. M7s became a familiar sight at Waterloo where they regularly worked on station pilot duty. None of the class worked beyond 1964. Power Classification 2P, Driving Wheel 5ft 7in, Cylinders inside.

Number	Name	Class	Type	Ex Works	Builder	Ex BR	Location	Status 2009
30053		M7	0-4-4T	1905	9Elm	1964	Swang (37)	Operational
30245		M7	0-4-4T	1897	9Elm	1962	NRM	Static display

N15 4-6-0 'King Arthur' No 777, seen on North Wales Coast Express duty on a perfect summer's day in 1991.

N15 4-6-0 'King Arthur' No 777 (BR 30777) is pictured in preservation, approaching Chester on a wet August day.

N15 LSWR locomotives were more commonly called 'King Arthurs'; they were designed by Urie and developed further by Maunsell originally for the LSWR, and then for the SR between 1918 and 1927. BR took into stock 74 of the express passenger engines and allocated the class numbers in the series 30448 to 30457, 30736 to 30755 and 30763 to 30806. Not including the batch converted to oil burning (WWII) and then converted back to coal, there were seven distinct variants. The original 30 engines were built at Eastleigh between 1918 and 1925 thereafter 30 of the class (including the preserved example) were built by North British Locomotive Co Ltd during 1925 followed by a further batch of 14 engines at Eastleigh between 1927 and 1927. Preserved example No 30777 Sir Lamiel was one of the so-called 'Scotch Arthurs' built by the NBL Co Ltd and coupled with an eight-wheel tender; it was withdrawn by BR in October 1961. No 30777 is a National Collection engine. Power Classification 5P, Driving Wheel 6ft 7in, Cylinders outside.

Number	Name	Class	Type	Ex Works	Builder	Ex BR	Location	Status 2009
30777*	Sir Lamiel	N15	4-6-0	1925	NB	1961	NRM	Operational

*SR number 777.

Q 0-6-0 class engines were Maunsell's last design for the SR and 20 of the class were built between 1938 and 1939. BR inherited all 20 allocating them the number series 30530 to 30549. Loco No 30541, the preserved example, was withdrawn from BR service in October 1964. The class was one of the last 0-6-0 types to be built in Britain, and although designed by his predecessor, Bulleid oversaw their production. Power Classification 4F, Driving Wheel 5ft 1in, Cylinders inside.

Number	Name	Class	Type	Ex Works	Builder	Ex BR	Location	Status 2009
30541		Q	0-6-0	1939	Elh	1964	Bbell (2)	Rebuild

Left: 'S15 Class' 4-6-0 No 841 (SR number, BR number 30841) pictured at work on the NYMR in 1986. Following a later rebuild this loco took on the identity of sister engine 825 (SR number).

S15 LSWR class locomotives were originally designed by Urie for the LSWR and introduced between 1920 and 1921, later Maunsell further developed the design for the SR in 1927; the SR built further engines in 1936. BR took 45 engines into stock and allocated the loco's numbers in the series 30496 to 30515, 30823 to 30847. The class were given both eight-wheel tenders 30496 to 30515, 30823 to 30832, 30838 to 30847 and six-wheel tenders 30833 to 30837, additionally locos 30504 to 30510 were given smaller eight-wheel tenders. The last year in which representatives of the class worked for BR was 1965, all the preserved examples were withdrawn during 1964. Power Classification 6F, Driving Wheel 5ft 7in, Cylinders outside.

'S15' 4-6-0 No 30506 is seen at Woodhams' scrapyard, Barry, in August 1974. This loco returned to steam on the Mid Hants Railway and ran for 14 years before being withdrawn pending a further rebuild.

Number	Name	Class	Type	Ex Works	Builder	Ex BR	Location	Status 2009
30499		S15	4-6-0	1920	Elh	1964	ELR (109)	Restoration
30506		S15	4-6-0	1920	Elh	1964	MHants (11)	Rebuild
30825*		S15	4-6-0	1927	Elh	1964	NYMR (99)	Operational
30828		S15	4-6-0	1927	Elh	1964	MHants (11)	Rebuild
30830		S15	4-6-0	1927	Elh	1964	NYMR (99)	Restoration
30841*		S15	4-6-0	1936	Elh	1964	NYMR (99)	See *
30847		S15	4-6-0	1936	Elh	1964	Bbell (2)	Rebuild

*During the last major overhaul of the locomotive No 30841 the frames and other parts of No 30825 were used and the operational loco was then given that number.

S15' No 30841 seen in the Woodham Bros scrap line prior to being rescued.

SEATON JUNC

T9 'Greyhound' 4-4-0 No 120 (BR 30120) as returned to LSWR livery in 1962, seen at Eastleigh.

T9 LSWR class locomotives were the famous London & South Western Railway 'Greyhound Class' designed by Drummond and introduced between 1899 and 1901. Between 1922 and 1929 they were rebuilt by Urie. BR took into stock 66 of the class and allocated them numbers in the series 30113 to 30122, between 30280 and 30338, 30702 to 30733. They were highly successful engines often to be seen working express services between Salisbury and Exeter. The last to be withdrawn was 30120 (July 1963) having been restored and repainted in LSWR livery in March 1962 in order to work special trains. Power Classification 2P reclassified 3P in 1953. Driving Wheel 6ft 7in, Cylinders inside.

T9 locomotive No 30120 (SR number) is pictured in BR service marshalling stock at Padstow in June 1961. *David Anderson.*

Number	Name	Class	Type	Ex Works	Builder	Ex BR	Location	Status 2009
30120		T9	4-4-0	1899	9Elm	1963	B&W (25)	Static display

USA 0-6-0T 'Switcher' No 30072 pictured in BR Guildford Loco shed in March 1966.

USA 0-6-0T 'Switcher' No 30065 is pictured in BR service at Eastleigh in 1963.

USA was the common name given to a batch of tank locomotives built for the SR under a War Department ruling. They were supplied during 1942 and 1943 by the Vulcan Ironworks USA and HK Porter USA and BR took into stock 14 examples, 13 of Vulcan Ironworks manufacture and one from HK Porter. They were given SR numbers 30061 to 30074 and several were later (1962/3) transferred to the 'service loco' pool being given numbers DS233 to DS238. When first entering service these engines took over the duties of the 'then' time-expired Adams 'B4' tanks at Southampton Docks. They are a typical USA 'Switcher' ie shunting loco design and accordingly had a wheel base of only 10ft. Power Classification 3F, Driving Wheel 4ft 6in, Cylinders outside.

Number	Name	Class	Type	Ex Works	Builder	Ex BR	Location	Status 2009
30064		USA	0-6-0T	1943	V	1967	Bbell (2)	Static display
30065*	Maunsell	USA	0-6-0T	1943	V	1962	K&ESR (9)	Operational
30070*	Wainwright	USA	0-6-0T	1943	V	1962	K&ESR (9)	Stored o/u
30072		USA	0-6-0T	1943	V	1967	K&WVR (95)	Stored o/u

*Became 'Service Locos' DS 237 (30065) and DS 238 (30070)

British Steam

'Schools' 4-4-0 No 928 Stowe (SR number, BR number 30928) in Southern Railway livery.

V 'Schools' class locomotives were designed by Maunsell for the Southern Railway and introduced into traffic between 1930 and 1935. BR took into stock all 40 of the class and allocated them numbers in the series 30900 to 30939. Built at Eastleigh the 'Schools' were the last design of a 4-4-0 type to be put into service in Britain. They were designed as three-cylinder locomotives with similar hauling power to the two-cylinder 'King Arthurs', but were lighter and therefore had wider route availability. The whole of the class were named after public schools. BR started scrapping the class in 1961 (only 25 survived to the end of that year) and all were taken out of service before the end of 1962. Power Classification 5P, Driving Wheel 6ft 7in, Cylinders three.

Number	Name	Class	Type	Ex Works	Builder	Ex BR	Location	Status 2009
30925	Cheltenham	V	4-4-0	1934	Elh	1962	NRM	Static display
30926	Repton	V	4-4-0	1934	Elh	1962	NYMR (99)	Operational
30928	Stowe	V	4-4-0	1934	Elh	1962	Bbell (2)	Rebuild

0415 LSWR class locomotives were built between 1882 and 1885 for the LSWR, they were designed by Adams. BR took into stock only three of these locos, two which had always been LSWR/SR engines and one which was sold in 1919 by the LSWR to the East Kent Railway and then purchased back by the SR in 1946. All three were kept in service to work the Lyme Regis branch of BR Southern Region. The engines took turns to work the branch for a week at a time, out of turn they were stored at Exmouth Junction shed. When the Exmouth Junction depot was taken over by the GWR in 1961 the 0415 tanks were withdrawn and replaced on Lyme Regis duty by 2-6-2T Ivatt locos. Power Classification 1P, Driving Wheel 7ft 7in, Cylinders outside.

Number	Name	Class	Type	Ex Works	Builder	Ex BR	Location	Status 2009
30583		0415	4-4-2T	1885	N	1961	Bbell (2)	Static display

0298 LSWR class locomotives were similar to many other 2-4-0T locos designed by Beattie specifically for suburban work in and around London. BR inherited only three of the class which were then numbered 30585 to 30587. They were modified three times, first by Adams, then by Urie and finally by Maunsell between 1931 and 1935. They were kept in service to work the Wadebridge-Wenford Bridge mineral branch line in Cornwall until replaced by GWR '1366' locos. All three were earmarked for preservation when withdrawn in 1962 but loco No 30586 somehow slipped through the net. Power Classification 0F, reclassified to 0P, in 1952. Driving Wheel 5ft 7in, Cylinders outside.

Right: **Class '0298' 2-4-0WT (Well Tank) loco No 30585 is pictured in BR service at Wadebridge in June 1961.** *David Anderson.*

Number	Name	Class	Type	Ex Works	Builder	Ex BR	Location	Status 2009
30585		0298	2-4-0WT	1874	BP	1962	BRC (16)	Operational
30587		0298	2-4-0WT	1874	BP	1962	B&W (25)	Operational

C SECR class locomotives were designed by Wainwright and introduced between 1900 and 1908 by the SECR. The original build total was 109 engines of which BR took into stock 106. They were allocated numbers in the series 31004 to 31725. These freight locos served the Southern Region of BR well and were even recorded at speeds of 70mph when pressed into service on passenger trains. By 1960 the number in service was halved and only three examples made it beyond 1962, although two of the class did serve as 'service locos' up to 1966. The preserved example was withdrawn in July 1963. Power Classification 3F reclassified to 2F in 1953. Driving Wheel 5ft 2in, Cylinders inside.

Number	Name	Class	Type	Ex Works	Builder	Ex BR	Location	Status 2009
31592		C	0-6-0	1902	Lngh	1963	Bbell (2)	Operational

D SECR class locomotives were designed by Wainwright as one of his standard classes and introduced between 1901 and 1907. The original build total was 51 engines of which 21 were rebuilt as 'D1 Class' between 1921 and 1927. BR took into stock 28 engines but none served beyond 1956. They were allocated numbers in the series 31057 to 31750. They were very elegant engines as first introduced with high quality paintwork and burnished brass dome covers which earned them the name 'Coppertops'. Power Classification 1P, Driving Wheel 6ft 8in, Cylinders inside.

Left: On shed. Loco No 31737 SECR Wainwright 'D Class' 4-4-0, with locos No 563 LSWR Adams T3 4-4-0 and 'A1 Terrier' No 82 Boxhill (Both preserved but neither passed into BR ownership).

Number	Name	Class	Type	Ex Works	Builder	Ex BR	Location	Status 2009
31737		D	4-4-0	1901	Asfd	1956	NRM	Static display

H SECR class locomotives were designed by Wainwright as another of his standard classes and were built between 1904 and 1915. Their designated work was suburban passenger traffic. These locomotives carried a distinctive Pagoda type cab and several of the class were fitted for 'push pull' working. BR inherited 64 of the original build total of 66 engines and they were allocated numbers in the series between 31005 and 31554. Three of the class survived to work into 1964 but not beyond. Power Classification 1P, Driving Wheel 5ft 6in, Cylinders inside.

Number	Name	Class	Type	Ex Works	Builder	Ex BR	Location	Status 2009
31263		H	4-4-0	1905	Asfd	1964	Bbell (2)	Static display

N SECR class locomotives were an SECR/SR design by Maunsell, introduced between 1917 and 1934. BR inherited 80 of these mixed traffic Moguls and allocated them numbers in the series 31400 to 31414, 31810 to 31821 and 31823 to 31875. Scrapping started in 1962 and six examples survived into the last year of SR steam. Power Classification 4MT when taken into BR stock reclassified to 4P5F in 1953. Driving Wheel 5ft 6in, Cylinders outside.

Number	Name	Class	Type	Ex Works	Builder	Ex BR	Location	Status 2009
31874		N	2-6-0	1925	Asfd	1964	MHants (11)	Rebuild

Right: **Preserved Maunsell 'N Class' No 31874 is pictured in Woodham Bros scrap line, before being rescued for preservation.**

Superbly restored ex SECR 'C Class' No 592 (BR number 31592) is seen with a period observation coach at home on the Bluebell Railway. *Paul Pettitt.*

Built in 1902 'C Class' 0-6-0 No 592 shows no sign of age, pictured on the Bluebell with a authentic rake of carriages and a milk tank. *Paul Pettitt.*

O1 SECR class locomotives were the first design by Stirling for the South Eastern Railway, introduced between 1879 and 1899. They were later rebuilt under the direction of Wainwright and BR took into stock 55 of the class, a total which included three locos which had been sold by the SECR to the East Kent Railway. The class was allocated BR numbers in the series 31003 to 31439. Power Classification 1F, Driving Wheel 5ft 2in, Cylinders inside.

Number	Name	Class	Type	Ex Works	Builder	Ex BR	Location	Status 2009
31065		01	0-6-0	1896	Asfd	1961	Bbell (2)	Operational

P SECR class locomotives were small tank engines designed by Wainwright for 'rail motor' work on branch lines. There were eight of these engines introduced between 1909 and 1910. BR took into stock all of them, but none of the class remained in service beyond 1961. Surprisingly four of the eight were preserved. Power Classification 0F, Driving Wheel 3ft 9in, Cylinders inside.

Right: **Wainwright SECR 'P Class' 0-6-0T No 753 (SE&CR number) pictured at the Kent & East Sussex Railway. This historically important loco carried SR number 1556 and BR number 31556, it is the oldest of the four preserved 'P Class' engines being outshopped from Ashford Works in 1909.** *Paul Pettitt.*

Number	Name	Class	Type	Ex Works	Builder	Ex BR	Location	Status 2009
31027		P	0-6-0T	1910	Asfd	1961	Bbell (2)	Rebuild
31178		P	0-6-0T	1910	Asfd	1958	Bbell (2)	Restoration
31323		P	0-6-0T	1910	Asfd	1960	Bbell (2)	Rebuild
31556		P	0-6-0T	1909	Asfd	1961	K&ESR (9)	Operational

Wainwright SECR 'P Class' 0-6-0T No 323 (SR number 1323, BR number 31323) pictured in the shed yard at Sheffield Park. *Paul Pettitt.*

Maunsell Mogul No 1638 (BR number 31638) seen at the loco's home base on preservation Golden Arrow duty. *Paul Pettitt.*

U SECR/SR class locomotives are unusual in that they were created by the rebuilding of the 'K1 River' class 2-6-4T locos, a class introduced between 1917 and 1925. The 'Us' were allocated BR numbers in the series 31610 to 31639 and 31790 to 31809. At Sevenoaks in August 1927 'K1' No 800 River Cray derailed at speed and the serious incident led to the whole class being withdrawn. There was no positive proof that the loco was at fault, indeed a later enquiry sited a track defect as the likely cause of the crash. Subsequently Maunsell 'U Class' Mogul 'rebuilds' were introduced between 1928 and 1934. BR took into stock 50 of the class which they started scrapping in 1962, four examples worked into 1965 but not beyond. Power Classification 4MT reclassified in 1954 to 4P3F. Driving Wheel 6ft 0in, Cylinders outside.

Number	Name	Class	Type	Ex Works	Builder	Ex BR	Location	Status 2009
31618		U	2-6-0	1928	Bton	1964	Bbell (2)	Static display
31625		U	2-6-0	1929	Asfd	1964	MHants (11)	Rebuild
31638		U	2-6-0	1931	Asfd	1964	Bbell (2)	Operational
31806		U	2-6-0	1928	Bton	1964	MHants (11)	Rebuild

No 31638 (SR 1638) now at the Bluebell, is seen in Woodham Bros' Barry scrap line, in the company of another rescued 'U Class' loco No 31625.

Maunsell Mogul No 1638 (BR number 31638) was built at Ashford and introduced in May 1931; it was taken out of BR service in January 1964, pictured on the Bluebell Railway. *Paul Pettitt.*

A1X LBSCR class locomotives were designed by Stroudley for the LBSCR and 50 were introduced between 1872 and 1880, 17 of which were rebuilt by Marsh between 1911 and 1947. BR took into stock 12 of the class and allocated them numbers in the series 32635 to 32678, W8, W13 (Isle of Wight) and DS377, DS515 and DS681 (service locos). The last in service were withdrawn following the closure of the Hayling Island Branch, at that time the A1Xs were the oldest ex LBSCR locomotives still at work on BR (November 1963). These diminutive tank engines had interesting and varied careers. Power Classification 0P, Driving Wheel 4ft 0in, Cylinders inside.

Left: The picture says it all! A1X 0-6-0T Stepney, among the spring flowers. *Barry Dewdrey.*

Number	Name	Class	Type	Ex Works	Builder	Ex BR	Location	Status 2009
32636	Fenchurch	A1X	0-6-0T	1872	Bton	1963	Bbell (2)	Operational
32640	Newport	A1X	0-6-0T	1878	Bton	1963	IoW (8)	Rebuild
32646	Freshwater	A1X	0-6-0T	1877	Bton	1963	IoW (8)	Rebuild
32650	Sutton	A1X	0-6-0T	1876	Bton	1963	SpVa (15)	Rebuild
32655	Stepney	A1X	0-6-0T	1875	Bton	1960	Bbell (2)	Static dispaly
32662	Martello	A1X	0-6-0T	1875	Bton	1963	Bressingham	Static display
32670	Bodiam	A1X	0-6-0T	1872	Bton	1963	K&ESR (9)	Operational
32678	Knowle	A1x	0-6-0T	1880	Bton	1963	K&ESR (9)	Operational

32636 Worked for the Newhaven Harbour Company from 1898, returning to the SR in 1925.
36240 Worked in the IoW 1902 to 1947 as number W11 then returned to SR.
32646 Worked in the IoW as number W2 and then W8, returned to SR in 1949.
32650 Worked in the IoW 1930 to 1937 as W9 then returned to the SR.
32655 Was withdrawn in 1925 then returned to traffic in 1927.
32670 Sold to the Kent & East Sussex Railway in 1901, worked as KESR No 3, returned to BR in 1948.
32678 Worked in the IoW 1929 to 1946 as W14 then returned to the SR.

A1X 0-6-0T No 55 Stepney (BR 32655) leads No 672 Fenchurch (BR number 32636) in this delightful Southern scene at the Bluebell Railway. *John Bowers.*

0-6-0T Stepney seen as preserved, in this instance coupled with a superbly restored observation coach. *John Bowers.*

A1 ABSCR 'Terrier' class was the forerunner to the 'A1X Class' designed and built by Stroudley for the London Brighton & South Coast railway between 1872 and 1880. Only one of these engines came into BR ownership, albeit as a service locomotive. DS680 was withdrawn in 1962. Power Classification 0P, Driving Wheel 4ft 0in, Cylinders inside.

Number	Name	Class	Type	Ex Works	Builder	Ex BR	Location	Status 2009
DS680	Waddon	A1	0-6-0T	1876	Bton	1962	NRM Canada	Static display

DS680. Built as No 54 it was sold to the SECR in 1904 becoming No 751. The loco returned to the SR in 1932 and worked as the Lancing Carriage Works shunter. Although later rebuilt with an A1X boiler DS680 kept its original smokebox and chimney, thus retaining its A1 classification. There is another preserved LBSCR 'ClassA1' in preservation, No 82 Boxhill; this loco was withdrawn in 1946 and thus never came into BR stock. No 82 is a National Collection engine.

Left: Billington ex LBSCR 'E4 Class' 0-6-2T seen at Sheffield Park Station on the Bluebell Railway as No 473 Birchgrove (LBSCR number 473, SR number 2437, BR number 32473) *Paul Pettitt.*

E4 LBSCR class of locomotives were built between 1897 and 1903, designed by Billington, there were originally 75 engines built. BR took into stock 70 of the class allocating them numbers in the series between 32464 and 32520, 32556 to 32566 and 32577 to 32582. By the end of 1960 only 28 remained in service, the last four being withdrawn by BR during 1963. Power Classification 2MT, Driving Wheel 5ft 0in, Cylinders inside.

Below: Billington ex LBSCR 'E4 Class' 0-6-2T is pictured in BR Southern Region livery as loco No 32473. *Paul Pettitt.*

Number	Name	Class	Type	Ex Works	Builder	Ex BR	Location	Status 2009
32473	Birch Grove*	E4	0-6-2T	1898	Bton	1962	Bbell (2)	Rebuild

*Name carried in LBSCR/SR service.

Q1 SR class of locomotives were built in an Austerity style in 1942, engines designed by Bulleid for the Southern Railway. They were the most powerful 0-6-0 tender type locomotives to ever run in Britain. BR inherited 40 of the type allocating them numbers in the series 33001 to 33040. They were described as the ugliest 0-6-0 locomotives ever built, but aside from their odd looks it has to be said that they were extremely successful engines. BR began scrapping the class in 1963 and only three examples survived to run in 1966, but not beyond. The Q1s had BFB Boxpok cast steel wheels. Power Classification 5F, Driving Wheel 5ft 1in, Cylinders inside.

Number	Name	Class	Type	Ex Works	Builder	Ex BR	Location	Status 2009
33001		Q1	0-6-0	1942	Bton	1964	NRM	Static display

BB & WC SR class Battle of Britain and West Country Pacific locomotives were designed by Bulleid and introduced between 1945 and 1951, first by the Southern Railway and later by British Railways. BR inherited 70 BB/WC locos in 1948 but that total was raised by continued construction to 110 engines. The class were allocated BR numbers in the series 34001 to 34110. The origin of the 'BB/WC' locos stemmed from the fact that the Southern Railway needed an express locomotive with greater route availability and in order to fulfil that need Bulleid designed a 'scaled down' version of his first air smoothed Pacifics, the 'Merchant Navy Class'.

The West Country, Battle of Britain Class 7P5F 4-6-2s were built at both Brighton and Eastleigh works, between 1945 and 1947 under the SR, and from 1948 to 1951 by BR. Innovation was very much the Bulleid way and much has been written about the originality of his designs which included streamlining (which he called the Air Smoothed Casing) chain-driven valve gear immersed in an oil bath, American style 'Boxpok' type wheels, electric lighting and an all welded construction steel (not traditional copper) firebox.

The rebuilding of 60 of the class was decided upon and that project got under way in 1957. Essentially the rebuilding centred on the removal of the 'air smoothed casing' and the replacement of the chain-driven valve gear with more conventional equipment. Square smoke deflectors were added and many observers have since commented upon the similarity in looks between the rebuilt Bulleid locomotives and the BR Standard Pacifics.

A total of 29 rebuilt and seven unrebuilt examples entered 1967 in BR service, but none served beyond that year. No less than 20 of the class survived into preservation, 10 of each form ie rebuilt and unrebuilt, to date not all have been restored. Power Classification 6MT reclassified to 7P5F in 1953. Driving Wheel 6ft 2in, Cylinders three.

Rebuilt SR 'West Country' Pacific No 34027 Taw Valley. Pictured on North Wales Coast Express duty in July 1989

By contrast SR 'West Country' Pacific No 34007 Wadebride is pictured as restored at the Gloucester & Warwickshire Railway in 2008. *Pete Sherwood.*

Rebuilt SR 'West Country' Pacific No 34101 Hartland pictured at Goathland on the NYMR.

Still in BR service unrebuilt SR 'West Country' Pacific No 34007 Wadebride is pictured at Nine Elms depot in April 1963.

Number	Name	Class	Type	Ex Works	Builder	Ex BR	Location	Status 2009
34007	Wadebridge	WC	4-6-2	1945	Bton	1965	MHants (11)	Operational
34010 r	Sidmouth	WC	4-6-2	1945	Bton	1965	Swang (37)	Restoration
34016 r	Bodmin	WC	4-6-2	1945	Bton	1964	MHants (11)	Operational
34023	Blackmoor Vale	WC	4-6-2	1946	Bton	1967	Bbell (2)	Rebuild
34027 r	Taw Valley	WC	4-6-2	1946	Bton	1964	SVR (59)	Rebuild
34028 r	Eddystone	WC	4-6-2	1946	Bton	1964	Swang (37)	Operational
34039 r	Boscastle	WC	4-6-2	1946	Bton	1965	GCR (49)	Stored o/u
34046 r	Braunton	WC	4-6-2	1946	Bton	1965	WSR (39)	Operational
34051	Winston Churchill	BB	4-6-2	1946	Bton	1965	NRM	Static display
34053 r	Sir Keith Park	BB	4-6-2	1947	Bton	1965	Swang (37)	Restoration
34058 r	Sir Frederick Pile	BB	4-6-2	1948	Bton	1964	AVR (24)	Restoration
34059 r	Sir Archibald Sinclair	BB	4-6-2	1949	Bton	1966	Bbell (2)	Rebuild
34067	Tangmere	BB	4-6-2	1947	Bton	1963	Southall	Operational
34070	Manston	BB	4-6-2	1947	Bton	1964	Swang (37)	Operational
34072	257 Squadron	BB	4-6-2	1948	Bton	1964	Swang (37)	Rebuild
34073	249 Squadron	BB	4-6-2	1948	Bton	1964	ELR (109)	Scrap cond
34081	92 Squadron	BB	4-6-2	1948	Bton	1964	NNR (69)	Rebuild
34092	City of Wells	WC	4-6-2	1949	Bton	1964	KWVR (95)	Rebuild
34101 r	Hartland	WC	4-6-2	1950	Bton	1966	NYMR (99)	Rebuild
34105	Swanage	WC	4-6-2	1950	Bton	1964	KWVR (95)	Stored o/u

r Preserved in rebuilt form.

MN SR class locomotives were the first streamlined (Air Smoothed) express passenger locomotives built for the Southern Railway. They were designed by Bulleid and the first of the type was introduced by the SR in 1941. British Railways continued with the Merchant Navy Class 8P 4-6-2 building programme at the ex Southern Railway Eastleigh Works and turned out the last of the class in 1949. The 'Merchant Navy' class totalled 30 engines; they were allocated BR numbers in the series 35001 to 35030.

In common with the 'BB/WC' locomotives the 'Merchant Navy' engines were all built with innovations unique to Bulleid, Air Smoothed Casing, chain-driven valve gear immersed in an oil bath, American style 'Boxpok' type wheels, electric lighting and an all welded construction steel (not copper) firebox.

In theory the 'oil bath' should have been a maintenance fitter's dream but in fact it caused a great many more problems than it solved. The steel fireboxes had a less than satisfactory service life with the first 10 all being replaced after only seven years. On the credit side the class were a whole lot better performers than any other SR express passenger locomotives of the time and importantly the Merchant Navy's greatly reduced 'hammer blow' (and therefore track damage) considerably. The type was very popular with locomotive crews but not universally so with maintenance departments.

The Merchant Navy Class were all rebuilt by BR between 1956 and 1959. As with the 'Light Pacifics' the rebuilding centred on the removal of the air smoothed casing and the replacement of the chain driven valve gear with more conventional equipment. Square smoke deflectors were added. Eleven of the class passed into preservation but not all have to date been fully restored. Power Classification 7P reclassified as 8P in 1951. Driving Wheel 6ft 2in, Cylinders three.

'Merchant Navy' Pacific 4-6-2 No 35025 Brocklebank Line is seen in BR service leaving Axminster with a train for Exeter Central. *David Anderson.*

'Merchant Navy' 4-6-2 No 35018 British India Line is pictured at Exmouth Junction Shed as newly rebuilt in July 1956. The loco was undertaking trials on the heavy Atlantic Coast Express service. In 2008 this loco was still in scrapyard condition. *David Anderson.*

Number	Name	Class	Type	Ex Works	Builder	Ex BR	Location	Status 2009
35005	Canadian Pacific	MN	4-6-2	1942	Elh	1965	MHants (11)	Operational
35006	Peninsular & Oriental S. N. Co	MN	4-6-2	1942	Elh	1964	G&WR (48	Restoration In steam 2009
35009	Shaw Savill	MN	4-6-2	1942	Elh	1964	ELR (109)	Scrap cond
35010	Blue Star	MN	4-6-2	1942	Elh	1966	ColnV (63)	Scrap cond
35011	General Steam Navigation	MN	4-6-2	1944	Elh	1966	WSR (39)	Restoration
35018	British India Line	MN	4-6-2	1945	Elh	1064	Portland	Scrap cond
35022	Holland America Line	MN	4-6-2	1948	Elh	1966	Southall	Restoration
35025	Brocklebank Line	MN	4-6-2	1948	Elh	1964	GCR (49)	Restoration
35027	Port Line	MN	4-6-2	1948	Elh	1966	Southall	Rebuild
35028	Clan Line	MN	4-6-2	1948	Elh	1967	Stewarts Lane	Operational
35029	Ellerman Lines	MN	4-6-2	1949	Elh	1966	NRM	Static display*

In 1989 restored 'Merchant Navy' Pacific No 35028 Clan Line is pictured on main line duty with a North Wales Coast express working.

In BR blue livery preserved 'Merchant Navy' No 35005 Canadian Pacific is seen on the West Coast main line at Winsford with The Blackpool Belle.

O2 LSWR class of locomotives were built between 1889 and 1895 for the LSWR, to an Adams design. Sixty of the class was originally built but BR only took into stock 48 of them. They were allocated BR numbers in the series 30177 and 30236 plus Isle of Wight numbers W14 to W36. The last 10 examples worked in BR service into 1966, but not beyond. Power Classification 1P reclassified to 0P in 1953. Driving Wheel 4ft 10in, Cylinders inside.

Left: **Adams '02' 0-4-4T W24 is pictured in BR service taking water at Ryde IoW.**

Number	Name	Class	Type	Ex Works	Builder	Ex BR	Location	Status 2009
W24	Calbourne	O2	0-4-4-T	1891	9Elm	1967	IoW (8)	Rebuild

NEW BUILDS
WORK IN PROGRESS

H2 LBSCR Atlantic a class of six engines developed and modified by Billington from an earlier Marsh design for the London Brighton & South Coast Railway in 1911/12. BR took six of these engines into stock and the last in service was 32424 Beachy Head, withdrawn in April 1958 and cut up a month later. No 32424 was also the last

Atlantic loco (4-4-2) to run in service for BR, that name and number have been chosen for the replica locomotive.

The Bluebell Railway announced on 29 October 2000, its intention to reconstruct a Brighton H2 Atlantic based on SR/BR period look of No 32424 Beachy Head.

Number	Name	Class	Type	Start date	Builder	Donor	Location	Status 2009
32424	Beachy Head	H2	4-4-2	2000	Bluebell Railway		Bbell (2)	Work in progress

H2 LBSCR Atlantic No 32424 Beachy Head, was withdrawn in April 1958 and cut up a month later. No. 32424 was also the last Atlantic loco (4-4-2) to run in service for BR, that name and number have been chosen for the replica locomotive. No 32424 is pictured at Brighton in 1957.

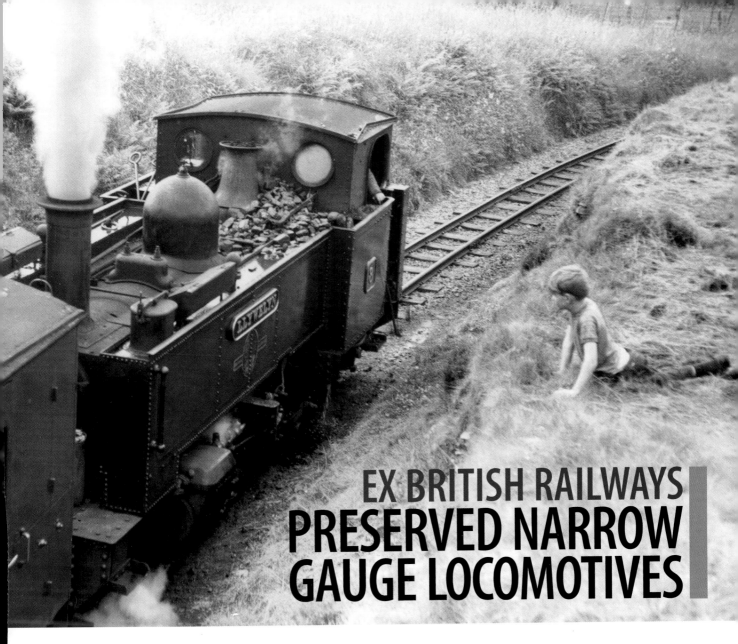

EX BRITISH RAILWAYS
PRESERVED NARROW GAUGE LOCOMOTIVES

VALE OF RHEIDOL RAILWAY

The Vale of Rheidol narrow gauge railway (1ft 11½ ins) in west Wales has the unique distinction of being the last bastion of BR steam. Although national network steam-hauled services were discontinued in August 1968 by British Railways they continued to operate steam locomotives on a tourist route which they inherited from the Great Western Railway in 1948. The Vale of Rheidol Narrow Gauge Railway consists of 11¾ miles of track set in stunning scenery between the Cambrian coastal town of Aberystwyth and Devil's Bridge (Pontarfynach) on the edge of Snowdonia.

The once independent line was amalgamated with the Cambrian Railway in 1902 and became part of the GWR in 1922. There were at that time two steam

locomotives No 1 *Edward VII* and No 2 *Prince of Wales*, which under GWR lost their names and became numbers 1212 and 1213. Those engines were joined by Swindon-built 2-6-2Ts numbers 7 *Owain Glyndwr* and 8 *Llywelyn* in July 1923. Another new engine was introduced by the GWR in 1924 and listed by the railway as a rebuild of 1213, at that time number 1212 was scrapped. BR renumbered 1213 as number 9 and reapplied the name *Prince of Wales*. The three Swindon-built locomotives, which became BR Class 98 were the only steam locomotives to carry BR Standard Blue livery. Although not currently in that livery all three locomotives are still based on the line, which was sold by BR to new owner/operators the Brecon Mountain Railway, in 1989.

Above: **The young boy is fascinated with VoR No 8 Llywelyn at Devil's Bridge in this captivating 1970s study.** *David Anderson.*

Number	Name	Class	Type	Ex Work	Builder	Ex BR	Location	Status 2009
7	Owain Glyndwr	98	2-6-2T	1923	Sdn	1989	VoR (85)	Stored o/u
8	Llywelyn	98	2-6-2T	1923	Sdn	1989	VoR (85)	Operational
9	Prince of Wales	98	2-6-2T	1923	Sdn	1989	VoR (85)	Operational

Left: BR Standard Blue loco and coaches, No 9 Prince of Wales prepares to leave Aberystwyth in July 1972.

Right: No 7 'running around' at Devil's Bridge.

Below: On the way up! Locomotive No 7 Owain Glyndwr, among the trees.

Corris No 4 Edward Thomas hard at work on the scenic Talyllyn Railway which runs through the Fathew Valley between Towyn (Gwynedd) and Nant Gwernol.

CORRIS RAILWAY LOCOMOTIVES – TALYLLYN RAILWAY

The crew of No 4 change the section token with the 'blockman' at Brynglas loop on the Talyllyn Railway.

The Corris Narrow Gauge Railway in mid-Wales once ran between the slate quarries near to the village of that name and a standard gauge railhead at Machynlleth, crossing a tidal stretch of the river Dovey. The 2ft 3in gauge line came into Great Western Railway ownership in 1930. In the winter of 1948 the Dovey railway bridge was washed away stranding the two Corris steam locomotives at the exchange sidings in Machynlleth, an event which led to the closure of the Corris Railway.

The two 0-4-2ST locomotives, numbered 3 and 4 respectively, were bought by the burgeoning Talyllyn Railway in 1951. Interestingly the locomotives carried the same numbers under four different ownerships, Corris Railway, GWR, BR and now Talyllyn. Both engines can be seen in action on the Talyllyn with Falcon Engine & Carriage Co-built No 3 carrying the name *Sir Haydn* and *Kerr Stuart* & Co Ltd-built No 4 named *Edward Thomas*. Nearby a short section of the original Corris Railway (location 75) still exists and is operated as a tourist railway often utilising a 'new build' steam locomotive created in the style of Corris No 4. A combined visit to both railways can be easily undertaken.

Number	Name	Class	Type	Ex Work	Builder	Ex BR	Location	Status 2009
3	Sir Haydn	Cor	0-4-2ST	1900	FE	1951	TyL (83)	Operational
4	Edward Thomas	Cor	0-4-2ST	1921	KS	1951	TyL (83)	Operational

WELSHPOOL & LLANFAIR RAILWAY

Passenger services on the 2ft 6in gauge Welshpool & Llanfair Railway were discontinued in 1931, however freight operations continued until the line's closure in 1956 when both of the railway's steam locomotives were placed in store. The originally independent line between Welshpool and Llanfair Caereinion was opened in 1903 and became part of the Cambrian Railway in 1922 and Great Western Railway in 1948. The W&L was reopened in 1963 by the Welshpool & Llanfair Light Railway Company.

The original two steam locomotives were built by Beyer Peacock & Co Ltd in 1902 and rebuilt in 1930; they carried the numbers 1 and 2 respectively until the GWR renumbered them 822 and 823. No 2 was originally named *The Countess*, under the present ownership 822 is named *The Earl* while 823 carries the name *Countess*.

Number	Name	Class	Type	Ex Work	Builder	Ex BR	Location	Status 2009
822	The Earl	W&L	0-6-0T	1902	BP	1963*	W&L (88)	Under repair
823	Countess	W&L	0-6-0T	1902	BP	1963*	W&L (88)	Operational

*Taken out of service and placed in store 1956.

Looking resplendent in GWR livery 0-6-0T stands at the coaling stage of the Welshpool & Llanfair Railway.

Built in 1902 by Beyer Peacock & Co Ltd tank locomotive 823 was rebuilt and given a new boiler in 1930. Together with sister loco 822 the 0-6-0T was placed in store by BR in 1956, and subsequently bought in 1963 by the Welshpool & Llanfair Light Railway Company.

PRESERVED RAILWAY DIRECTORY

| STANDARD GAUGE | NARROW GAUGE | TRACK LENGTH | 22 | FOOTPLATE EXPERIENCE | L | WINE & DINE TRAINS | 🍽 |

SOUTH EAST

1 AMBERLEY WORKING MUSEUM ¼
Arundel, W Sussex
www.amberleymuseum.co.uk
Tel: 01798 831370

2 BLUEBELL RAILWAY 9 L 🍽
Sheffield Park, East Sussex
www.bluebell-railway.co.uk
Tel: 01825 720800

3 BREDGAR & WORMSHILL RAILWAY ½
Nr, Sittingbourne, Kent

4 EAST KENT RAILWAY 2 L
Shepherdswell, Dover
Tel: 01304 832042

5 EXBURY GARDENS RAILWAY 1¼ L
New Forest, Hampshire
www.exbury.co.uk
Tel: 0238 089 1203

6 HAYLING SEASIDE RAILWAY 1
Hayling Island, Hants
www.easthaylinglightrailway.co.uk

7 HOLLYCOMBE STEAM COLLECTION 1
Liphook, Hants
info@hollycombe.co.uk
Tel: 01428 724900

8 ISLE OF WIGHT STEAM RAILWAY 5
Havenstreet, Isle of Wight
www.iwsteamrailway.co.uk
Tel: 01983 882204

9 KENT & EAST SUSSEX RAILWAY 10½ L 🍽
Tenterden, Kent
www.kesr.org.uk
Tel: 01580 765155

10 LAVENDER LINE 1 L 🍽
Isfield, E. Sussex
www.lavenderline.co.uk
Tel: 01825 750515

11 MID-HANTS RAILWAY 10 L 🍽
Alresford, Hants
www.watercressline.co.uk
Tel: 01962 733810

12 ROMNEY, HYTHE & DYMCHURCH RAILWAY 13½ L
New Romney, Kent
www.rhdr.org.uk
Tel: 01797 362353

13 ROYAL VICTORIA RAILWAY 13½ L
Netley, Southampton
www.rhdr.org.uk
Tel: 0238 045 6246

14 SITTINGBOURNE & KEMSLEY LT. RAILWAY 1¾ L
Sittingbourne, Kent
Tel: 0871 222 1568

15 SPA VALLEY RAILWAY 4 L
Tunbridge Wells, Kent
www.spavalleyrailway.co.uk
Tel: 01892 537715

HOME COUNTIES

16 BUCKINGHAMSHIRE RAILWAY CENTRE ¼ L
Quainton Road, Bucks
www.bucksrailcentre.org
Tel: 01296 655720

17 CHINNOR & PRINCES RISBOROUGH RAILWAY
Chinnor, Oxon
www.cprra.co.uk
Tel: 01844 353535

18 CHOLSEY & WALLINGFORD RAILWAY 2½
Wallingford, Oxon
www.cholsey-wallingford-railway.com
Tel: 01491 835067

19 DIDCOT RAILWAY CENTRE L
Didcot, Oxon
www.didcotrailwaycentre.org.uk
Tel: 01235 817200

20 GREAT COCKROW RAILWAY
Hardwick Lane, Lyne, Chertsey
www.cockrow.co.uk
Tel: 01932 565474

21 EPPING-ONGAR RAILWAY 6
Ongar Station
www.eorailway.co.uk
Tel: 01277 365200

22 LEIGHTON BUZZARD RAILWAY 2¾
Leighton Buzzard, Beds
www.buzzrail.co.uk
Tel: 01525 373888

23 SOUTHALL RAILWAY CENTRE ¼
Southall, West London
www.gwrpg.co.uk
Tel: 0208 574 1529

SOUTH WEST

24 AVON VALLEY RAILWAY 3 L 🍽
Willsbridge, Glos
www.avonvalleyrailway.co.uk
Tel: 0117 932 7296

25 BODMIN & WENFORD RAILWAY 6½ L 🍽
Bodmin, Cornwall
www.bodminandwenfordrailway.co.uk
Tel: 01208 73666

26 DARTMOOR RAILWAY 3
Okehampton, Devon
www.dartmoorrailway.co.uk
Tel: 01837 55637

27 DEVON RAILWAY CENTRE ½
Bickleigh, Devon
www.devonrailwaycentre.co.uk
Tel: 01884 85567

28 EAST SOMERSET RAILWAY ?
Cranmore, Somerset
info@eastsomersetrailway.com
Tel: 01749 880417

29 GARTELL LIGHT RAILWAY 1
Templecombe, Somerset
glr-online.co.uk
Tel: 01963 370752

30 LAUNCESTON STEAM RAILWAY 4
Launceston, Cornwall
Launcestonsr.co.uk
Tel: 01566 775665

31 LYNTON & BARNSTAPLE RAILWAY 1
Woody Bay, N. Devon
www.lynton-rail.co.uk
Tel: 01598 763487

32 MOORS VALLEY RAILWAY 1
Ringwood, Hants
www.moorsvalleyrailway.co.uk
Tel: 01425 471415

33	**PAIGNTON & DARTMOUTH STEAM RLY**	7 Y
	Paignton, Devon	Tel: 01803 555872

34	**PLYM VALLEY RAILWAY**	½
	Marsh Mills, Plymouth, Devon	www.plmrail.co.uk

35	**SEATON TRAMWAY**	3 L
	Harbour Rd, Seaton, Devon	Tel: 01297 20375
	www.tram.co.uk	

36	**SOUTH DEVON RAILWAY**	7 L Y
	Buckfastleigh, Devon	Tel: 01364 642338
	www.southdevonrailway.org	

37	**SWANAGE RAILWAY**	6 L Y
	Swanage, Dorset	Tel: 01929 425800
	www.swanagerailway.co.uk	

38	**SWINDON & CRICKLADE RAILWAY**	1 L
	Blunsdon, Wiltshire	Tel: 01793 771615
	www.swindon-cricklade-railway.org	

39	**WEST SOMERSET RAILWAY**	20 L Y
	Minehead, Somerset	Tel: 01643 704996
	www.west-somerset-railway.co.uk	

MIDLANDS

40	**AMERTON RAILWAY**	1
	Stowe-by-Chartley, Staffs	Tel: 01785 850965
	www.amertonrailway.co.uk	

41	**BARROW HILL**	¼
	Chesterfield, Derbyshire.	Tel: 01246 472450
	www.barrowhill.org.uk	

42	**BATTLEFIELD LINE RAILWAY**	5
	Shackerstone, Leics	Tel: 01827 880754
	battlefield-line-railway.co.uk	

43	**CHASEWATER RAILWAY**	2
	Walsall, W. Midlands	Tel: 01543 452623
	www.chasewaterrailway.co.uk	

44	**CHURNET VALLEY RAILWAY**	5¼ L Y
	Cheddleton, Staffs	Tel: 01538 360522
	www.churnet-valley-railway.co.uk	

45	**DEAN FOREST RAILWAY**	4¼ L Y
	Norchard, Lydney, Glos	Tel: 01594 843423
	www.deanforestrailway.co.uk	

46	**ECCLESBOURNE VALLEY RAILWAY**	4
	Wirksworth, Derbys	Tel: 01629 823076

47	**FOXFIELD RAILWAY**	5½
	Blythe Bridge, Staffs	

48	**GLOUCESTERSHIRE WARWICKSHIRE RLY**	10 L Y
	Toddington, Glos	Tel: 01242 621405
	www.gwsr.com	

49	**GREAT CENTRAL RAILWAY**	8 L Y
	Loughborough, Leics	Tel: 01509 230726
	www.gcrailway.co.uk	

50	**MIDLAND RAILWAY - BUTTERLEY**	3½ L Y
	Ripley, Derbyshire	Tel: 01773 570140

51	**NATIONAL TRAMWAY MUSEUM**	1
	Crich, Derbyshire	Tel: 01773 852565
	www.tramway.co.uk	

52	**NORTH INGS FARM MUSEUM**	1
	Dorrington, Lincs	Tel: 01526 833100

53	**NORTHAMPTON & LAMPORT RAILWAY**	2
	Pilsford, Northants	Tel: 01604 820327
	nlr.org.uk	

54	**NOTTINGHAM TRANSPORT HERITAGE CTR**	4
	Ruddington, Notts	Tel: 0115 940 5705
	www.nthc.co.uk	

55	**PEAK RAIL**	4
	Matlock, Derbyshire	Tel: 01629 580381

56	**PERRYGROVE**	
	B4228, Coleford, Glos	Tel: 01594 834991

57	**RUDYARD LAKE RAILWAY**	1½
	Leek, Staffs	Tel: 01995 672280
	www.rudyardlakerailway.co.uk	

58	**RUTLAND RAILWAY MUSEUM**	¾
	Cottesmore, Rutland	Tel: 01572 813203

59	**SEVERN VALLEY RAILWAY**	16 L Y
	Bewdley, Worcs	Tel: 01299 403816
	www.svr.co.uk	

60	**STEEPLE GRANGE LIGHT RAILWAY**	½ L
	Wirksworth, Derbyshire	Tel: 01629 580917
	www.steeplegrange.co.uk	

61	**TELFORD STEAM RAILWAY**	½
	Telford, Shropshire	Tel: 07765 858348
	www.telfordsteamrailway.co.uk	

EAST ANGLIA

62	**BURE VALLEY RAILWAY**	9 L
	Aylsham, Norfolk	Tel: 01263 733858
	www.bvrw.co.uk	

63	**COLNE VALLEY RAILWAY**	1 L Y
	Castle Hedingham, Essex	Tel: 01787 461174
	www.cvr.org.uk	

64	**EAST ANGLIAN RAILWAY MUSEUM**	¼ L
	Wakes Colne, Essex	Tel: 01206 242524
	www.earm.co.uk	

65	**MANGAPPS RAILWAY**	1
	Nr Burnham on Crouch, Essex	Tel: 01621 784898
	www.mangapps.co.uk	

66	**MID-NORFOLK RAILWAY**	L 11½
	Dereham, Norfolk	Tel: 01362 690633
	www.mnr.org.uk	

67	**MID SUFFOLK LIGHT RAILWAY**	½
	Wetheringsett, Suffolk	Tel: 01449 766899
		01473 890622

68	**NENE VALLEY RAILWAY**	7½ L
	Wansford, Peterborough, Cambs	Tel: 01780 784444
	www.nvr.org.uk	

69	**NORTH NORFOLK RAILWAY**	5½ L
	Sheringham, Norfolk	Tel: 01263 822045
	www.nnrailway.co.uk	

70	**WELLS & WALSINGHAM LIGHT RLY**	4
	Wells-Next-The-Sea, Norfolk	Tel: 01328 711630

PRESERVED RAILWAY DIRECTORY

STANDARD GAUGE	▭	NARROW GAUGE	▪	TRACK LENGTH	22	FOOTPLATE EXPERIENCE	L	WINE & DINE TRAINS	ⓨ

WALES

71 BALA LAKE RAILWAY 4½
Llanuwchllyn, Gwynedd — Tel: 01678 540666
www.bala-lake-railway.co.uk

72 BARRY ISLAND RAILWAY 1½
Barry Island, South Wales — Tel: 01446 748816 office hrs

73 BRECON MOUNTAIN RAILWAY 3½
Merthyr Tydfil, Glamorgan — Tel: 01685 722988
www.breconmountain.co.uk

74 CAMBRIAN RAILWAY ½
Llyndys Junction, Oswestry — Tel: 01352 770413

75 CORRIS RAILWAY ¾
Maespoeth, Machynlleth — Tel: 01654 761303
www.corris.co.uk

76 FAIRBOURNE RAILWAY 2½
Fairbourne, Gwynedd — Tel: 01341 250362
www.fairbourne-railway.co.uk

77 FFESTINIOG RAILWAY 15
Porthmadog, Gwynedd — Tel: 01766 516000
www.festrail.co.uk

78 GWILI RAILWAY 2
Bronwydd Arms, Carmarthenshire — Tel: 01267 238213
01267 230666

79 LLANBERIS LAKE RAILWAY 3
Llanberis, Gwynedd — Tel: 01286 870549

80 LLANGOLLEN RAILWAY 7½ L ⓨ
Llangollen, Denbighshire — Tel: 01978 860979
www.llangollen-railway.co.uk

81 PONTYPOOL & BLAENAVON RAILWAY ½
Blaenavon, Torfaen — Tel: 01495 792263

82 SNOWDON MOUNTAIN RAILWAY 4½
Llanberis, Gwynedd — Tel: 01286 870223

83 TALYLLYN RAILWAY 7½ L
Tywyn, Gwynedd — Tel: 01654 710472
www.talyllyn.co.uk

84 TEIFI VALLEY RAILWAY 2
Henllan, Carmarthenshire — Tel: 01559 371077

85 VALE OF RHEIDOL RAILWAY 11¾
Aberystwyth, Cardiganshire — Tel: 01970 625819
www.rheidolrailway.co.uk

86 WELSH HIGHLAND RAILWAY 12
Caernarfon, Gwynedd — Tel: 01766 516000
www.festrail.co.uk

87 WELSH HIGHLAND RAILWAY (P) 1
Porthmadog, Gwynedd — Tel: 01766 513402
www.whr.co.uk

88 WELSHPOOL & LLANFAIR LIGHT RLY 8
Llanfair Caereinion, Mid Wales — Tel: 01938 810441
www.wllr.org.uk

NORTH EAST

89 APPLEBY-FRODINGHAM RLY PRES SOCIETY 2
Corus Steelworks, Scunthorpe, Lincs — Tel: 01652 657053
www.afrps.co.uk

90 BOWES RAILWAY 1
Gateshead, Tyne & Wear — Tel: 0191 416 1847
www.bowessrailway.co.uk

91 CLEETHORPES COAST LIGHT RLY 2
Cleethorpes, NE Lincs — Tel: 01472 604657

92 DERWENT VALLEY LIGHT RAILWAY ½
Murton Park, York

93 ELSECAR RAILWAY ½
Elsecar, S Yorks

94 EMBSAY & BOLTON ABBEY RAILWAY 5 ⓨ
Nr Skipton, N Yorks — Tel: 01756 794727
www.embsayboltonabbeyrailway.org.uk

95 KEIGHLEY & WORTH VALLEY RLY 5 L ⓨ
Keighley, W Yorks — Tel: 01535 645214
www.kwvr.co.uk

96 KIRKLEES LIGHT RAILWAY 4
Huddersfield, W Yorks — Tel: 01484 865727

97 LINCOLNSHIRE WOLDS RAILWAY ½
Ludborough, Lincs — Tel: 01507 363881

98 MIDDLETON RAILWAY 1½
Hunslet, Leeds — Tel: 0113 271 0320
www.middletonrailway.org.uk

99 NORTH YORKSHIRE MOORS RAILWAY 18 ⓨ
Grosmont, N Yorks

100 SOUTH TYNEDALE RAILWAY 2¼
Alston, Cumbria — Tel: 01434 382828
www.strps.org.uk 01434 381696

101 TANFIELD RAILWAY 3
Gateshead, Co Durham — Tel: 0191 388 7545
www.tanfield-railway.co.uk

102 WEARDALE RAILWAY 5½
Stanhope, Co Durham — Tel: 01388 526203
www.weardale-railway.org.uk

103 WENSLEYDALE RAILWAY 22
Leyburn, North Yorkshire — Tel: 08454 505474

SCOTLAND

104 BO'NESS & KINNEIL RAILWAY 3½
Bo'ness, W. Lothian — Tel: 01506 822298
www.srps.org.uk

105 CALEDONIAN RAILWAY 4
Brechin, Angus — Tel: 01356 622992
www.caledonianrailway.co.uk

Smoke, steam and frost! This evocative image is of ex LNER K1 2-6-0, 61994 The Great Marquess departing from Consall Forge Station on the Churnet Valley Railway. *David Gibson*

106	KEITH & DUFFTOWN RAILWAY	11
	Dufftown, Morayshire	Tel: 01340 821181

107	LEADHILLS & WANLOCKHEAD RAILWAY	1
	Leadhills, Stratchclyde	Tel: 0141 556 1061
	www.leadhillsrailway.co.uk	

108	MULL RAIL	1½
	Craignure, Isle of Mull	Tel: 01680 812494
	www.mullrail.co.uk	

109	STRATHSPEY RAILWAY	10
	Aviemore, Inverness-shire	Tel: 01479 810725
	www.strathspeyrailway.co.uk	

NORTH WEST

110	EAST LANCASHIRE RAILWAY	12 L
	Bury, Lancs	Tel: 0161 764 7790
	www.east-lancs-rly.co.uk	

111	GROUDLE GLEN RAILWAY	¾
	Isle of Man	Tel: 01624 622138 eves

112	ISLE OF MAN STEAM RAILWAY	15½
	Douglas, Isle of Man	Tel: 01624 663366
	www.iombusandrail.info	

113	LAKESIDE & HAVERTHWAITE RAILWAY	3½
	Nr Ulverstin, Cumbria	Tel: 01539 531594

114	RAVENGLASS & ESKDALE RAILWAY	
	Ravenglass, Cumbria	Tel: 01229 717171

115	RIBBLE STEAM RAILWAY	1½
	Preston, Lancs	Tel: 01772 728800

116	WEST LANCS LIGHT RAILWAY	
	Nr Preston, Lancs	Tel: 01772 815881

RAILWAY MUSEUMS

ABBEY PUMPING STATION
Leicester. Open: Sat-Wed
BARROW HILL ROUNDHOUSE
Chesterfield, Derbyshire. Tel: 01246 472450.
www.barrowhill.org.uk Open W/Es
BEAMISH
Co Durham. North of England Open Air Museum.
Open: Daily
BERE FERRERS STATION
Bere Ferrers, W Devon
Tel: 01822 840044. Open: W/Ends.
TYSELEY LOCOMOTIVE WORK
Tyseley, Birmingham. Tel: 0121 708 4960
www.vintagetrains.co.uk/brm.htm.
Open: Weekends
CAMBRIAN RAILWAYS SOCIETY
Oswestry Station. Open: W/Es
COL. STEPHENS RLY MUSEUM
Tenterden Station, Kent. Tel: 01580 765155
Open: KESR operating days

CONWY VALLEY RLY MUSEUM
Betws-y-coed, Conwy Tel: 01690 710568
Open: Daily
EAST ANGLIA TRANSPORT MUSEUM
Carlton Colville, Lowestoft
Tel: 01502 518459
Open: Sats, Suns, Weds & B/Hols.
GLASGOW TRANSPORT MUSEUM
Bunhouse Rd, Kelvinhall
Tel: 0141 2872720. Open: Daily.
IRCHESTER NARROW GAUGE RLY MUSEUM
Nr Wellingborough, Northants.
Open: Suns.
KIDDERMINSTER RAILWAY MUSEUM
Kidderminster, Worcestershire
Tel: 01562 825316
Open: SVR operating days.
LOCOMOTION: THE NATIONAL RAILWAY MUSEUM AT SHILDON
Co Durham. Open: Daily

LONDON TRANSPORT MUSEUM
Covent Garden Piazza. Open: Daily.
MIDSOMER NORTON
Silver Street, Midsomer Norton. Open: Suns/Mons.
MONKWEARMOUTH STN MUS
Sunderland, Co Durham.
Tel: 0191 567 7075. Open: Daily.
NATIONAL RAILWAY MUSEUM
York. Tel: 01904 621261. Open: Daily.
NORTH TYNESIDE RAILWAY
North Shields. Tel: 0191 200 7145 Running: Suns.
NORTH WOOLWICH OLD STATION MUSEUM
London E16. Tel: 0207 474 7244
Open: Weekends – 1pm-5pm.
ROYAL DEESIDE RAILWAY
Milton of Crathes, Banchory, Aberdeen.
Open: Weekends.
RUSHDEN RAILWAY MUSEUM
Rushden, Northants
Tel: 01933 318988. Open: Suns.

SCOTTISH INDUSTRIAL RAILWAY
Dalmellington, Ayrshire
Tel: 01292 313579 (eves/wkds). Open Suns
SOMERSET & DORSET RAILWAY TRUST
Washford, Somerset
Tel: 01984 640869. Open: Weekends.
STEAM – MUSEUM OF THE GWR
Swindon, wilts. Tel: 01793 466646 Open: Daily.
THE RAILWAY AGE
Vernon Way, Crewe
Tel: 01270 212130. Open: Weekends.
ULSTER FOLK & TRANSPORT MUSEUM
Cultra, Co Down. Open: Daily.
VINTAGE CARRIAGE MUSEUM
Ingrow, W Yorks. Tel: 01535 680425 Open: Daily.
WINCHCOMBE RAILWAY MUSEUM
Winchcombe, Glos
Tel: 01242 609305. Open: Wed-Sun.
YEOVIL RAILWAY CENTRE
Yeovil Junction, Somerset.

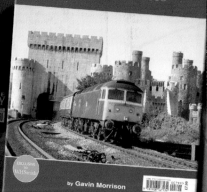

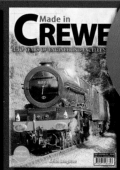